LIFE WITHOUT A CRUTCH

An Introduction to Recovery from Addiction

by

Linda Ingraham
Steve Bell
Ned Rollo

OPEN, INC. Information Series

SERIES EDITOR
Katherine S. Greene
OPEN, INC.

SPECIAL THANKS

OPEN, INC. extends our *deepest appreciation* to the following people for their contribution to the creation of this handbook:

Jack Anderson   Inmate, Pennsylvania Dept. of Corrections

Karren Baird-Olson   Instructor, Dept. of Sociology, Anthropology
                                  & Social Work, Kansas State University

John K. Burchill   Director
                                  Saline Co. Community Corr. Dept., Salina, KS

Jerry Cunningham   Chairman
                                  Texas Commission on Alcoholism and Drug Abuse

Dr. Robert Dain   Director
                                  Dallas Institute For Rational-Emotive Therapy

Nick Demos   Acting Chief - Special Initiatives Branch
                                  Office for Treatment Improvement
                                  Alcohol, Drug Abuse and Mental Health Admin.

Sandi Dennis   Dallas, TX

Mark Faust   Probation Officer
                                  Dallas Co. Community Supervision and Corr. Dept.

Dr. Jawad Fatayer   Instructor of Criminal Justice
                                  West Texas State University, Canyon, TX

Dr. Gary Field   Manager of Alcohol and Drug Abuse Services
                                  Oregon Dept. of Corrections

Glenn A. Graves   Counselor, Drug Abuse Program
                                  Tallahassee Federal Correctional Institution

Connie Gray   Administrator for Outpatient Services
                                  The Ethel Daniels Foundation

Dr. Clyde Hanks   Dallas, TX

Emmitt Hayes   Criminal Justice Specialist
                                  Texas Commission on Alcoholism and Drug Abuse

SPECIAL THANKS (CONTINUED)

William Hobby
Substance Abuse Program Director
Pardons and Paroles Division
Texas Dept. of Criminal Justice

Dr. Alan Ingram
Clinical Psychologist
Seagoville Federal Correctional Institution

Geoff Lucas
School Principal, State Correctional Institution at
Smithfield, Pennsylvania Dept. of Corrections

Susan Ann Kane
Parole Agent, California Dept. of Corrections

Dr. Sally Lancaster
Vice President & Grants Coordinator
The Meadows Foundation, Dallas, TX

Robert Neuman
Corr. Counselor, Kettle Moraine Corr. Institution
Wisconsin Dept. of Corrections

Maggie Noth
Supervisor
Dallas Co. Community Supervision and Corr. Dept.

Mel Segal
Chief - Program Development Branch
Office of Substance Abuse Prevention
Alcohol, Drug Abuse and Mental Health Admin.

Barbara Swift
Director, Substance Abuse Treatment Program
Institutional Div., Texas Dept. of Criminal Justice

John Sykes
Coor., Alcoholism & Drug Abuse Counseling Prog.
Dallas Co. Community Supervision and Corr. Dept.

John Tartaro
Director, The New Place, Dallas, TX

Jerry Vigdal
Director, Office of Drug Programs
Wisconsin Dept. of Corrections

Terry Walton
Inmate, Pennsylvania Dept. of Corrections

NOTE

We wish to offer special recognition and thanks to the wealth of anonymous clients and recovering addicts whose wise counsel and verbal quotes we so generously used throughout this text.

FOREWORD

Addiction to drugs, alcohol, crime, as well as other substances and behaviors, is a common problem for thousands of men and women involved in our correctional systems. The addictions control them until they become slaves to these substances or actions. As slaves to addiction, they are cut off from the joy of life and their own opportunity to relate in a healthy way to themselves and others. They become self-destructive — mere shells of their true selves as non-addicted persons.

In **Life Without a Crutch,** the authors discuss how addicted individuals can take the first step toward recovering their own person. Addicted individuals and families do that by confronting their denial of the problem. The addict knows that something is wrong and so does his or her family. What's wrong is that lives are enslaved by the addiction in a vicious cycle of destruction.

The authors provide information about how both the addict and those who care for him or her can confront the addiction and begin to get help. They suggest several types of help and emphasize that each of us needs that help in order to recover from addictive behavior. Help, however, only really "helps" if we stay determined to take control of our own lives. Help is available when people tell us the truth and when we tell the truth to ourselves.

Addiction distorts our lives and muddles our thinking. It keeps us frightened and disabled, but still we'd rather not face it. Like a ball rolling down a hill, addiction is hard to stop. The authors provide a way to face the addiction and take that first step toward reclaiming our lives.

Recovery is more than abstinence. It is bringing joy and balance back into our lives. It is fighting constant temptation with perseverance as we learn to respect ourselves and others. The primary objective of recovery is to build healthy ways of living and relating.

In clear and concise language, the authors help addicted individuals and their families find a way to face the truth and reclaim the person who has become the slave to addiction.

Eric Dlugokinski, Ph.D.
Professor
Dept. of Psychiatry and Behavioral Sciences
Oklahoma University Health Sciences Center

ABOUT THE AUTHORS

LINDA INGRAHAM, PH.D.

Linda Ingraham received her Ph.D. in Psychology from Ohio State University and is currently in private practice as a forensic psychologist in Dallas, Texas. She is a member of the American, Texas and Dallas Psychological associations. She holds a Certificate of Proficiency in the Treatment of Alcohol and Other Psychoactive Substance Disorders from the American Psychological Association and is also a Registered Sex Offender Treatment Provider.

Dr. Ingraham has worked extensively with correctional clients, including those who have addictive problems. She often appears as an expert witness in both criminal and civil cases.

STEVE BELL

Steve Bell is an assistant supervisor with the Community Supervision and Corrections Department in Dallas, Texas. He is also pastor of the First Missionary Baptist Church in Terrell, Texas. He graduated in 1980 from Tennessee Temple University in Chattanooga, majoring in Bible and Psychology, and in 1996 graduated from Dallas Baptist University with an MA degree in Counseling. He has over 14 years experience in criminal justice and substance abuse counseling.

Steve Bell provides training seminars on addiction before religious and civic organizations as well as substance abuse treatment facilities. He also conducts substance abuse prevention programs in public schools throughout Texas.

NED ROLLO

Ned Rollo is an ex-offender and recovering addict, as well as a correctional counselor and staff trainer with 32 years experience in the corrections field. He is the creator and a principal author of the OPEN Information Series, a collection of self-help books of which this book is a part. The OPEN Information Series is currently in use in over 500 institutions and programs across the nation.

Ned Rollo has served over five years in state and Federal prisons for manslaughter, possession of drugs and firearm violations. He is a 1971 graduate of Roosevelt University in Chicago, Illinois, with a degree in Psychology. Since founding OPEN, INC. in 1979, he has counseled over 30,000 offenders and trained correctional treatment staff in 20 states.

TABLE OF CONTENTS

OFFICIAL NOTICE

INTRODUCTION

ADDICT! What images does this nasty little word bring to mind? A drunk, face down in his own vomit? A junkie, over-dosed with a rig still in his arm? Or some lurking pervert in search of an unsuspecting victim?

Whatever our mental picture of an "addict," it is not good or desirable. We probably imagine someone vastly different from ourselves, a shifty sub-human who would sell his or her soul to satisfy unnatural cravings. But is this *really* what an addict looks like? Before we can understand the trap of addiction, we must get a clear picture of who an "addict" really is.

While some people are born with physical traits which make it easy for them to become addicted, *most* are **not.** The authors believe that most people **learn** to be addicted. First, they discover that something they do can help them feel good or keep them from feeling bad — at least for a while. Then, by repeating the action people become dependent on their "crutch," using it more and more just to stay even. This effort to get relief or pleasure gradually takes control, destroying their freedom to make choices and becoming a kind of mental slavery.

Addictions are powerful habits that can overwhelm most anyone. But since we can learn to be addicted, we can also learn to gain control and redirect our lives. It is possible to find fresh, more rewarding ways to feel good and handle problems. The process of growing beyond addiction is what we will call **"recovery."** It is a path of self-discovery and pride that a person can follow to reach his or her highest potential. No one is born with the knowledge and strength required to make this journey alone. To succeed in this quest, most people need special help in the form of guidance and support.

Life Without a Crutch is an *introduction to recovery from addiction.* It describes what addiction is, its causes and effects, the rewards of overcoming it, and ideas on how to begin. Please keep in mind that this is a guide to recovery but not *through* recovery. This book will guide you to the river but it's up to you to build the raft needed to get across.

Once you decide it is time to live addiction-free, the question is "how?" As you will see in the section **Finding the Right Help,** many kinds of treatment exist. You must be prepared to reach out and use the best help available to you. No matter what you select or what is available, it is *your* commitment that will unlock a new world of power and pride.

People can get "strung out" in countless ways and the process described in this book applies to most of them. However, **Life Without a Crutch** is written mainly for the person whose addictions can lead or have led to *problems with the law.* If you are already caught up in the criminal justice system, you may want help or be required to get treatment. If so, you will find this book an ideal place to begin.

Life Without a Crutch is also for people who are not addicted but suffer from the effects of addiction on a family member or loved one. People who care about an addict must also struggle toward a new and better life. This book can help you understand the process of addiction and what you can do (and should *not* do) to assist yourself and encourage your loved one.

These pages reflect the joy of reclaiming yourself from the bondage of addiction. Your recovery is a valuable chance to look inside yourself and discover the very best you can be. Please use this book as a stepping stone to find the help you need. Beyond the struggle you will find great rewards. Let there be no doubt: it can be done and you can do it!!

CHAPTER ONE

WHAT IS ADDICTION?

It is always hard to decide when a certain way of thinking or behaving has become an addiction instead of a choice. The dictionary defines addiction as "the giving up of one's self habitually." By this definition, any behavior can be addictive if it controls the individual, rather than the individual controlling the behavior.

Addiction involves a special "cycle" or predictable pattern of thinking and behaving which captures a person a little more each time it is repeated. The first phase in gaining freedom from addiction is to understand what "addiction" is and how it works.

CONTROL IS THE KEY

"Addiction is like a thief in the night! Sometimes it takes a little, sometimes a lot, but it never gets enough. It keeps coming back for more until it owns you...all of you."

How can we tell the difference between an act that is done often and an act that is addictive? The distinction is whether the act controls the person or the person controls the act. The "avid" golfer may prefer to stay out on the course, but he or she will make rational choices and be sure to take care of business. The "addicted" golfer will play even when lightning is striking all around him and his shoes are full of water; even when it means missing work or an important family event. He doesn't just want to play, he thinks he has to!

An "addict" is a person who surrenders control of him or herself on a habitual basis, thereby giving up their dignity, power, and quality of life. The addict loses the ability to make good choices. In the process he or she will ignore or explain away the negative results of his or her addictive behavior.

Anything Can Be Addicting

"Basketball! 24 hours a day, we played basketball!! Day and night, in our dreams, during school, after school, weekdays, weekends and holidays, we moved the ball up and down the court!"

When the word addiction is mentioned, we immediately think of drugs and alcohol. Actually, a person can become addicted to any behavior, such as sexual acting out, murder, playing pool, eating chocolate, or gambling. People can also be addicted to working, cat raising, stamp collecting, shopping, exercise, or almost any activity that one can imagine. All of these behaviors sound very different. But for the people addicted to them, they have two things in common: 1) they are done to excess and 2) they cause problems in the lives of the people addicted to them.

Remember that an addiction is formed when a person gives him or herself up to a certain behavior; this gives the behavior more power over a person than they have over themselves. But how could a behavior as harmless as stamp collecting affect a person's life in such a negative way? Well, consider the following.

- Our stamp collector has spoiled many a relationship because she couldn't tear herself away from her stamps to spend time with her family and friends. And when they do get together, all she wants to talk about is her collection.
- Her bills are behind because of all the money she spends on stamps.
- She has sold family heirlooms to buy more stamps. She feels bad about that and lies to her brothers when they ask about an item.
- She has been late for work several times because she stayed up most of the night working on her collection. Often when she is at work, she is so tired that she doesn't do a good job.
- In the shower, at church, in the car, and sometimes while making love, she is thinking about stamps!
- She may even turn to illegal behavior to feed her addiction. For instance, she might embezzle money from her work to buy that special stamp. Of course she sees it as a small loan and means to pay it back. When she can't pay it back, she may rationalize that she deserves the money.

The Trap Closes Slowly

"Addiction is like a vise that closes real slowly. You ignore it until there is no way to wiggle free."

Addictive behavior tends to develop slowly. This is one reason we usually fail to see it coming. At first, the stamp collector just bought stamps every once in a while and only spent a few hours a week thinking about it. But after awhile she began to get lost in it, letting other things slide in order to pursue her hobby. It was a great escape from the demands of everyday life. As the hobby grew, she became obsessed, filling her home with books, storage folders, and magazines related to stamps. In short, she became driven to collect stamps no matter what it did to the rest of her life!

Or, you may smoke a joint because others are doing it or it just seemed like a good idea at the time. It feels good, so you try it again and then begin to buy your own stash. Slowly it becomes part of daily life and you make sure that you have it with you when you travel or attend an event. After awhile, you may choose friends because they also like to get high. As you become addicted, you sometimes develop a whole routine around smoking. You may have a favorite pipe, buy only a certain brand of rolling papers, keep a roach clip on your key chain, make a special stash box for your dope and equipment, and even have a special way of cleaning the pot. You collect these habits and items slowly until they are just a part of your life and you no longer think about them. One day you wake up to the fact that the first thing you do in the morning and the last thing you do at night is light up a joint!

Then there is the person who begins to drink only on a social basis, then at dinner, then after work, then at lunch, then to "relax." Soon you make sure booze is available when you want it, which is more and more of the time. There is no intent to become a drunk, just a wish to "take the edge off" of the stress of daily life. The next thing you know, many important decisions are being made under the influence of alcohol. Again, it didn't happen overnight.

Another example is a sex addict. When the routine of a person with a strong sexual habit is examined, not only are there special people, places, and events that become part of their addiction, but also special thoughts and feelings. By repeating the same type of act or fantasy, it becomes ever more powerful and compelling. One man's fantasy was to see a teenage girl and envision her coming on to him. After a few years it became a thought which never left his mind. It drove him to seek out young girls time after time, even at the expense of his marriage, health, and professional reputation.

It's very important to understand that thoughts and feelings themselves are a part of the addictive routine. Eventually the thoughts, places, sensations, special details, paraphernalia, or whatever become part of the package and are performed in an automatic, unconscious way. The thought process is part of the addiction — whether a person is thinking about snorting cocaine, eating a double cheeseburger, robbing a Pizza Hut, stopping at a bar, shoplifting, or buying a rare stamp.

IS IT ILLEGAL OR IMMORAL?

"Right or wrong, good or bad, if it runs you, you're a slave!"

The basic damage of addiction is not based on whether the behavior is good or bad, moral or immoral, legal or illegal. It is the destructive nature of addiction itself that causes problems. If an addicted person loses control of his or her behavior in a way that endangers others or breaks the law, that behavior is obviously wrong or illegal. And we usually think of addictive behavior as bad, immoral, illegal, or unacceptable. However, people can become addicted to almost anything, including behavior that is legal, moral, socially acceptable, and even popular.

For example, we usually think of drug abuse when we think of addiction, but smoking cigarettes can also be a powerful addiction. Smoking cigarettes is usually legal, while smoking marijuana is not. Overeating is not generally considered immoral, but it can certainly be an addiction.

Some behavior such as drinking alcohol is usually legal, but may lead to illegal actions such as driving while intoxicated. If a drunk driver causes an accident or death, we consider his or her behavior both illegal and immoral.

Other behaviors may be either legal or illegal, depending on how they are carried out. Collecting stamps is a legal and acceptable activity, but it becomes illegal and wrong if a stamp collector steals to support his or her habit. For another example, seeking power can be an addiction for some people. A person who seeks power by becoming a policeman may be just as much a power junkie as someone who holds a group of hostages at gunpoint to get the rush of total control.

Some people are addicted to more extreme types of behavior, for instance random violence, rape, and murder. These acts are definitely illegal, immoral, and wrong. Actually, it may not be the act that is addictive, but rather the adrenaline rush that it gives. Adrenaline is a natural chemical produced by the body at times when we are in danger or excited. For people addicted to this "kick," it may take a very extreme action such as robbery, rape, or even murder to feed their habit.

The point is, addictive behavior is harmful regardless of whether it is legal or illegal, moral or immoral, accepted or not. When an addictive behavior is considered illegal or immoral, it may lead to social disapproval or a legal problem. This can result in rejection by society or a ticket, fine, or arrest that can be very damaging. But the greatest destruction caused by addiction falls on the addict him or herself. The loss of control and power does the ultimate damage!

WHO IS HURT?

"I really tried to quit smoking when I was pregnant with Buddy, but after a few days I'd get weak. He was born five weeks early and has been real sick. They tell me it was because of the crack."

The danger of addictions and the damage they cause are on two levels: the effects on the addict him or herself and the effects of the addict's behavior on other people. In some cases, our addictions reach out and touch the lives of many, many people.

Some addictions affect mainly the individual who has the habit. An example would be the compulsive overeater; he or she may hate being heavy and may have health problems because of the weight. Also, because eating becomes an escape, a way to forget about troubles, the addict's life may be filled with unsolved problems.

Other addictions may hurt the addict and the people closest to him or her. For instance, compulsive gambling eats up the whole family's resources. Being strung out on extreme displays of behavior such as anger, sexual desire, or ambition often has a negative impact on family and friends. Use of addictive chemicals during pregnancy can lead to very serious health problems in the unborn child. In fact, many babies today are born addicted to illegal drugs. Being close to an addict can become a living hell for everyone involved!

There are also addictions that may be offensive to people in general. For example, cigarette smoke smells bad and may bother other people's breathing or irritate their eyes. Although this kind of addiction causes problems mostly for the individual and the people around him or her, some people might claim that it also hurts society in an indirect way. A smoker or an overeater may have health problems that will increase the costs of health care for everyone.

Finally, some kinds of addictive behavior pose a direct threat to society in general, for example when an alcoholic becomes violent and attacks the people around him. Or when a hot-check writer gets strung out on beating people out of their money. Or when an HIV-positive addict shares needles. An extreme example is the thrill killer whose victims become unwilling parties to a deadly addiction. The public is also affected if an addict's habit becomes so expensive that he or she turns to robbery or burglary to feed that habit.

The public's reactions to addictions are strongly influenced by the harm they cause. As society sees more and more damage created by various addictions, people become less and less tolerant!

HOW TO THINK LIKE AN ADDICT

We like to believe our thoughts and feelings are "special." It's a way to see ourselves as unique and valuable. And obviously those of us with an addiction problem are individuals with our own unique ways of doing things. But no matter what our differences, we all wrestle with confused thinking, out-of-control behavior, and the problems that result.

Our first weapon in the fight against addiction is the discovery that addictive thoughts and actions are highly predictable! That is, despite their different addictions and personalities, the behavior of a person with an addiction often follows a pattern similar to the behavior of other addicts. And these patterns tend to have a negative impact on many other aspects of our lives. By growing ever more aware of these patterns, we can watch ourselves and others dancing the same tired steps over and over.

Many of the following examples may not fit you exactly, but most of the reactions surely will. Middle-class or hard core, you'll find a lot of yourself here! So as you read, open your mind and heart. Let this be a private moment of truth: ask yourself how much of YOUR thinking is tied up with addiction.

***

"Good drugs and good loving are hard to come by. When you snooze you lose, so when it's time to party I'm going to be first in line!"

As addicts, we tend to be impulsive. We are driven by the craving for immediate pleasure or quick relief. This extreme hunger for instant gratification leads us to follow our first impulse with little or no thought given to the results. Our first response is often to engage in our addictive behavior in order to prepare for any other experiences. We tell ourselves that it's OK to do whatever moves us, without stopping to consider the consequences.

***

"I love to GO REAL FAST! Sometimes I scare the hell out of myself, especially when the whole boat goes airborne. Then I'm just dancing on the waves...pushing it right to the edge!!"

5

We often live in a world of intense feelings, going to extreme measures to get a rush. This is especially true if we are danger, sex, or love junkies, or power and success addicts. If so, we are always looking for situations which are a bit more intense than the last time. Danger is the way some addicts know that they are "really alive." It can reach a point where anything less than living on the edge is viewed as dull and not worth doing.

***

*"When my bike is running good it's a rush better than sex,
but when it's down I want to use it for a boat anchor!"*

Our addiction may distort our thinking so that we see no middle ground. Everything is black or white: it's either awesome or it's the pits. Words like "contented," "satisfied," or "annoying" aren't even in our dictionary. If we have a flat tire, we may decide it's a total disaster. We've got to "fix" the situation right NOW! If we can't get a new tire installed on the spot, then we will settle for a shot of our addiction to relieve the pressure. Since we are overwhelmed by extreme feelings so much of the time, we may not have enough energy left to solve our problems.

***

*"My mamma didn't raise me to sweep no floors. They make
me shop foreman or I'm outta here!!"*

We may also go to the extreme of all-or-nothing thinking. If there's a problem with the rent, we've got to have all the rent money or it's no good. We may never think of paying part and asking for more time to pay the rest.

We may have the same problem when setting goals for ourselves. We tend to jump from the first to the last step and ignore all the steps in between. This is okay for simple tasks, but it doesn't work for a big project. You can't rebuild a motorcycle without tearing it down and chasing replacement parts first. Any major goal is reached the same way: by identifying the middle steps toward that goal and carrying them out in order.

***

"All I want is everything NOW! Is that so much to ask!?"

Impatient, all-or-none thinking can lead us to defeat ourselves in other ways. We tend to want everything to happen right now. We may not be able to stand even a little frustration before getting angry or giving up. Even when we have a realistic idea of what needs to be done, we tend to schedule too much and expect it to happen too soon. This way we defeat ourselves and feel like failures; then we need more of our addiction to forget how bad we feel.

Expecting too much too soon can really hurt when we are trying to build relationships with other people. Comfort and trust just cannot be developed overnight.

"I came home after five years in prison expecting to get a good job, buy a new car, find a sweet woman and get a nice place to live...all in the first six months! But what I found was a minimum wage gig at a gas station, a city bus, a flea bag hotel and seven car loads of loneliness. I just didn't know how to handle the disappointment. The next thing you know I was back off into shooting junk."

Many addicts are perfectionists with unrealistic expectations of themselves — we have too many "shoulds" in our lives. Again we set ourselves up for failure by expecting or demanding too much. For example, if we believe we should be able to find a high-paying job in two weeks, we will feel lower than dirt when we are still unemployed a month later. Our self-esteem suffers when we don't meet our expectations, even though they were unrealistic.

We tend to "fix" low self-esteem and the resulting bad feelings by turning to our addiction. This fix refers to more than just drug and alcohol use. It can be whatever lightens the load, giving us short-term relief from our pain. Sex addicts, as an example, are more likely to act on their urges when their self-esteem suffers. Compulsive shoppers are more likely to load up the credit cards when they are feeling low.

***

"She took everything so personally! One night she overcooked our dinner; when I didn't eat it all she went completely crazy, turned the table over and stormed out the door."

We also tend to be very sensitive and to over-react to situations. We expect other people to hurt us and often get upset without waiting to see if they really will harm us. We may take everything personally and get defensive at even the slightest hint of criticism. If someone mentions that smoke bothers their eyes, addicts are offended and assume they have been put down for smoking.

When we don't get our way, we may assume the other person is angry or out to get us. Some of us become so good at taking offense that we become addicted to the anger inside. We then feed our rage by looking for more and more ways that other people hurt or offend us. Of course, we believe our raging is someone else's fault.

***

"SURE, I was going the wrong way down a one-way street with my lights off, but if he'd been alert he wouldn't have run into me. Hey, he looked right at me before he hit me — the idiot!"

We usually see what happens to us as someone else's fault. We try to avoid responsibility by placing our fate in the hands of others or blaming other people when something goes wrong. When someone fails to take good enough care of us or won't cover up our mistakes, it gives us an excuse to get our feelings hurt and go feed our addiction.

In the process, we create countless ways to avoid taking care of our own needs. This is done by mind games and emotional manipulation — such as playing the helpless victim role — and by forms of emotional blackmail, including threats of self-destruction. Nobody is better at guilt trips and self-pity roles than addicts looking for some chump to "fix" or carry them.

**

"After Arthur wrecked the car his mom gave him, he borrowed her car every night — until he wrecked it, too. Now Arthur borrows his sister's car and mom rides the bus."

When we get lost in addiction, we lose our concern for the feelings and well-being of other people. By placing the burden of uncontrolled actions on someone else's shoulders, an addict can become a world-class user of others. It's as though people exist just to help us feed our addiction! In short, we can become self-centered jerks. If this gets out of hand and we've burned everyone we know, our family and friends get so bitter and afraid they simply won't trust anything we do or say.

**

"I don't have a drinking problem! Hell, I'm young and healthy; for me, two fifths a weekend is normal!"

Addiction thrives on deception. It's amazing how many ways addicts can find to lie to themselves! We will tell ourselves we are always in total control, that we can stop anytime, that it's all somebody else's fault, that it's really no big thing, that our behavior is even necessary and normal. In this way, we conspire against ourselves in order to stay addicted. This is a serious betrayal of ourselves, because we are most vulnerable when we don't see or accept the truth. Our refusal to face reality may lead us to lose everything we value, especially ourselves.

**

"Poor Dave, too much is never enough!"

An addictive rush is temporary, just a fleeting spark. So it's always too short and incomplete. And because the relief or pleasure is usually more wishful thinking than fact, an addict can never be satisfied. There is always a drive for MORE! Just one more drink, one more hit, one more climax, one more deal — it's like trying to put out a fire by pouring gas on the flames. The more we do, the more we want. Each effort to "get enough" pulls us deeper into habitual behavior and the frustration of greater unmet needs.

CHAPTER TWO

EFFECTS OF ADDICTION

Now that we have described addiction and how an addict sees the world, we need to get a true understanding of the *effects* of addiction on ourselves and others. This may sound boring, but it is VITAL that we have a clear picture of the damage addiction brings about! Until we really see what is happening to us, we won't find the strength to fight back.

EFFECTS ON YOURSELF

"Sex, drugs and rock and roll could solve ALL my problems if life only lasted a few hours. But when I come down everything is still right here waiting for me, worse than before!"

People use addictive behavior to fulfill a "need": it helps them control painful feelings or it makes them feel good for a while. It causes an immediate change in the way we feel, and the change is predictable — something we can count on. We gradually surrender our freedom of choice in exchange for instant pleasure or escape. In the process, we give up other activities that could really *fulfill* our needs.

Although our addictive behavior may relieve pain and frustration for the moment, it also cuts a person off from the joys of life and the satisfaction of resolving problems. In many cases the result of addictive activity is not pleasure but just numbness, the absence of any feeling at all. The substance or behavior can serve as a pain-killer, **but it won't solve the problem that caused the pain.** This is very important. It's like taking an aspirin instead of getting a tooth filled.

Behavior which was intended to solve a problem has become a new problem itself. It can reach the point where you can ask an addict what, besides his addiction, is enjoyable, and he or she will just give a blank stare. Other forms of recreation and personal fulfillment have been smothered as the addiction takes over the addict's existence. With all satisfaction gone except for the addiction, life becomes dull and empty.

Chasing an Illusion

"It was exciting as hell the first time I did crack. Jesus, what a rush!! My whole body left the floor and I felt like Superman jumping over tall buildings!"

The high an addiction gives is an illusion. An addict will tell you there is no high like the first high. However, the desire to repeat that first experience is so strong that a person will not give up. He or she keeps thinking, "Maybe this time, it'll be as good...." It never is. You're only a virgin once.

In alcoholism, a drinker may develop a "hollow leg;" it seems to take more and more to get drunk. Then one day the dose that gets him or her high exceeds all limits and causes physical collapse. Even in the addictions that do not use a substance, such as sex or power, a constant increase in behavior is needed to satisfy the growing desire.

An addiction left unchecked is a bottomless pit. The more you feed and ignore it, the larger and faster it grows! It continues to demand more of you while offering less in relief or satisfaction. Finally there is nothing left but a memory of what was.

Surrender of Self-Esteem

> *"It's hard to think of yourself as a child of God when you feel like cow dung on the bottom of somebody's boot."*

Addiction, remember, is loss of control. An addicted person feels **driven** to pursue a habit even while it is consuming his or her life! This feeling of being powerless is humiliating and deeply depressing. So whenever a person feels out of control, their self-worth takes a nose dive. As an addiction consumes more of a person's life, the addict's self-esteem continues to shrink until he or she feels about the size of an ant!

As an example, a person who has the need to expose himself in public knows that others think he is perverted. But he believes that he can't stand the frustration he will feel if he doesn't do it. Because he can't control the way he expresses his needs, he will destroy any sense of mastery or pride he has left.

Self-esteem suffers equally when you realize that a white powder, a person, a bottle, or any addiction runs your life, not you. When you realize you have lost control, you feel mounting stress. And by now you **know** how to relieve stress. In fact, the first and perhaps only way you can think of to relieve stress is to indulge in your addictive behavior. So it becomes a vicious circle.

Loss of Identity

> *"When I'd look in the mirror, there wasn't anybody there!"*

When you lose your self-worth, you vanish! Once you regularly experience the loss of control over your own life, you begin to lose identity. One of the major ways we identify ourselves is by what we do. We think of ourselves in terms of what we spend most of our time doing. If you spend a good deal of your time driving a truck, you think of yourself as a truck driver. If you also spend time being a parent, you think of yourself as a parent. In fact, you think of yourself in many roles at once and take part of your identity from each.

As your addiction takes up more and more of your life, you struggle even harder to escape the facts of your captivity and loss of control. This denial — refusing to face yourself and the nature of your addiction — eats up whatever is left of your self-esteem. You **know** you're living a lie when you refuse to face the truth!

Of course you won't think of yourself as an addict at first — no one ever does! In fact, you probably will become disgusted and feel bad about the things you do as an addict long before you admit you are "addicted." For instance, you may feel bad about lying to your spouse or stealing from a co-worker. This feeling bad about yourself leads to even lower self-esteem, in turn creating more discomfort. So you increase your addictive behavior in the false hope of relief. This is a deadly cycle!!

Finally there is no corner left to hide in. Something happens which brings you face to face with the FACT that you are out of control. Perhaps it's an alcoholic blackout, breakup of your marriage, arrest, an overdose, unwanted pregnancy, or auto accident. No matter what the event, from this point on, you begin to suspect that you are inadequate or less than a whole person without your addiction.

This is especially true as your addictive behavior leads to problems that may cause you to lose your job. Then you no longer have the job as an identity. And since you may not spend as much time with your children, you may think of yourself less in terms of being a parent. Once you reach the point where most of your time is spent pursuing your addiction, you can't avoid thinking of yourself as an addict — at least in your innermost self.

Clearly being an addict is not a positive role. Thinking of ourselves in this negative way will continue to destroy our self-esteem until our identity is just a memory of someone we used to know.

Isolation

"Even in a crowd, I was alone. Even at the moment of sexual climax, I was alone. It was always the same – I was the only person on the planet."

Addiction is a very personal "secret" that we hide both from ourselves and from others as long as we possibly can. One way we know we've got a problem is when we catch ourselves sneaking off to do our thing. If our addiction is illegal or immoral, we work especially hard to see that no one knows. We often feel shame and guilt about what we are thinking and doing. These feelings set us even more apart from others.

Of course friends and family may try to stick with us despite our behavior. They can and often do bail addicts out…until they simply run out of patience and hope! Friends and loved ones can also run out of funds or get so disgusted with flaky behavior, self-pity, and childish demands that they refuse to help. This leaves us pretty much alone.

Or maybe we are alone by choice. We may not go near our loved ones because we're ashamed of our behavior or of being arrested because of it. We often get so sad and depressed over our behavior that we pull away and hide. This is very dangerous because it puts us even more at the mercy of our addictive escapes and distorted thinking. We may even think that our addiction is our only true friend.

The longer we are separated from our friends and loved ones, the easier it becomes to justify the separation. At first we just don't have time. Then we make it their problem: "They don't understand me," "Squares bore me," or "All they do is nag." Actually, it may be more comfortable for us to be alone or to hang out with people who share our addiction.

One common result of isolation is feeling that we are **totally unique** and no one can understand what we are going through. This deadly trap leads to withdrawal from the world. We continue to isolate ourselves, becoming increasingly cut off from our real feelings and needs, as well as from the world around us. With no way to "test" our mental and emotional reality, we become ever more vulnerable to our addictions. As a result, we turn to them more and more for relief from our loneliness. And with each repetition we become more strung out, more captive, and more isolated!

Depression

> *"Patty was more of a pancake than a person! After a few years she turned into a human downer, just existing, never really giving a damn about herself or anything else."*

Maybe you've tried to quit several times. Perhaps you've even been successful for months at a time. But you always come back to your addiction — sometimes because you faced a difficult situation, sometimes because you got with some old running buddies or participated in an activity you used to do when you were high. Whatever the trigger, depression or desire, you came back. **Again** you resigned yourself to not being in control of your life. In this way you accepted your helplessness. This failure and expanded loss of control does GREAT damage to your sense of self-worth.

Sometimes you have been successful at stopping a particular addiction only to find that you have shifted your behavior, or substituted one addiction for another. At such times it's easy to get discouraged and say, "What's the use?!"

When you become resigned or give up, you feel hopeless and helpless. This brings with it a condition called depression. Depression steals your strength and makes you even more ineffective in dealing with life. You don't feel like getting up or getting dressed. Even opening the drapes to let in the light seems like too much effort. This makes you feel even more depressed. A deep depression almost never goes away by itself. It is a sign of your grief when you give up on yourself and lose your hope. Depression is very serious because it robs a person of the energy and will to overcome it.

If you are addicted to certain drugs or alcohol, they also add to your depression. Alcohol is a depressant, while cocaine, for example, uses up the supply of the brain chemical that allows us to feel happy. This is why the high of cocaine is followed by the crash.

Hopelessness

"Fun died, laughter died, love died. Nothing mattered any-more...NOTHING at all. I couldn't see any reason to go on...why bother??"

The cruelest and most dangerous effect of addiction is the loss of hope! Without hope, we can see no reason to go on living. Our lives lose their meaning. When this happens, our addiction has handed us a bitter defeat: it has kidnapped our very souls, our will to live. What greater loss can anyone endure? And for **what?**

Poor Health

"I lost all contact with my body...just sorta living in it and waiting to be evicted. It wasn't really mine, if you know what I mean, so there wasn't any reason to take care of it."

Substance and eating addictions have a direct effect on health. Examples are the effects on the brain caused by alcohol and drugs and the known health problems caused by obesity. But even if your addiction is not to a substance, addictions take their physical and mental toll. Engaging in your addiction takes time and energy and produces great stress and anxiety. This leaves you less time and self-organization to attend to your diet, mental health, exercise, emotional stability, and sleep. The financial cost of an addiction leaves less money to go to your doctor when you're sick; the tendency is to put off medical care or the counseling that would help you deal with major problems.

Financial Problems

"First your money, then your clothes, then your old lady goes."

An addict may not only lack the funds for health care, he may spend so much on his addiction that he doesn't have money to take care of everyday business. Financial problems are especially bad for compulsive gamblers, drug addicts, and a wide array of spending addicts. An addict's intention to pay bills is easily overcome! If the bill isn't due today, it is easy to pretend the money will somehow turn up when it is due. This "magical thinking" probably ignores the fact that the next paycheck is already committed to other bills. Addicts may lose their car, apartment, etc., but they get very good at rationalizing that these things weren't important anyway.

Some addicted people play a different money game with themselves. They do pay their basic expenses, but they hold back money for their addiction with no concern for their future needs. This way, they never get ahead of the game, but they can fool themselves into believing they are being responsible. When their car needs fixing, their shoes wear out, or their child needs clothes, they see this as "bad luck." They don't admit that these are predictable events which they could plan for, if they truly acted responsibly.

If your addictions lead to legal problems, they will become an even greater drain on your finances. You will need to pay lawyers' fees and bail money. If convicted, you may have to pay court costs, fines, or probation fees, if you are lucky. Otherwise, you may have to sit the time out in jail or prison. At this point, you will probably have spent all your money and lost the job which was your means of earning money.

Loss of Freedom

"My life became a box that seemed to get smaller every day. One night I realized there was no corner left to hide in...I was dying, body and soul."

The ability to be independent and govern one's self is a very precious part of a rewarding life. Bit by bit addiction erodes our independence, turning us into slaves. An addiction takes a big world and shrinks it down until it would fit in a bottle! At this point, we are totally consumed by our obsession and its effects.

Being possessed by our addiction can be deadly within our minds and hearts and in social and legal ways as well. If our addiction has been defined as "criminal," we run the ever-increasing risk of losing our physical freedom for years to come. As bad as this is, however, it is minor compared to the loss of our self-control, dignity, and self-worth.

The danger is that we surrender ourselves just one little drop at a time. One thought, one feeling, one act. Yet with each seemingly unimportant event, our addiction drains away our mental, physical, and spiritual freedoms. It is critical that we be alert and never be a willing party to our own slavery!!

EFFECTS ON YOUR FAMILY

We Miss You!

"Daddy hardly ever makes it home for supper anymore; and when he does get in, we have to help him up the stairs and put him to bed."

Like it or not, you are always somebody's parent, child, brother or sister, aunt, uncle, cousin, or grandparent until the day you or they die. No matter how far away you get, you will always be a member of your family. For better or worse, your family gave you the starting point for the person you are today. And just as your family has influenced you, your behavior will always have an impact on them.

As your addiction has grown, whatever role you have in the family has been changing. First, you took on the role of "addict," seriously shifting the lines of responsibility and power. As you become more involved with your

addiction, you will change. You may seem like an entirely different person —
someone they don't even know.

Since you gave up control over your addiction, your family is having to
deal with an **emotional child**. They will clearly see your behavior as imma-
ture and self-destructive, and will have trouble understanding how you could
act this way. They may have to put up with a lot of irresponsible behavior from
you, take over your responsibilities, or make choices for you they don't want
or like. If you are in jail or prison, they have the added burden of trying to support your financial, emotional, and legal needs. In some cases, they may have
to protect themselves if you try to use or abuse them. This is not a role that
people are pleased with or proud to acknowledge.

There But Not There

> *"He kept pulling back from me, more and more, until we were
> like strangers. Finally I discovered he had a 'new lady;' her
> name was Heroin."*

Some addictions are intolerant of **any** competition for your time and energy.
They leave you less and less energy to share with family members. The priorities
in your life gradually shift as family and friends take a back seat to the addiction. You probably try much harder to make time for your addiction than you try
to be with your family.

If your loved ones ask you to be closer and more considerate, you may get
angry or feel guilty. But you probably don't give them the closeness they are
asking for. After a while, they will get the message that your addiction is more
important to you than their love. They may feel rejected or abandoned by you.
Whether they draw back from you or try to stick with you, you have put a wall
between you and those who care the most about you.

Not Doing Right

> *"I don't know how to face my people when they come to visit
> me. They try to be nice but I know I've let them down. It isn't
> the first time and probably won't be the last."*

Since you became addicted, you feel different about yourself — and not
usually in a positive way. Your role as a positive influence in your family will
change, because you spend less time with them, you may behave irresponsi-
bly, and you feel less important when you are there. In fact, you may take on
the role of black sheep in your family. If you practice your addictive behavior
around your family, you have let them see a side of you that you would probably rather keep hidden. If you try to cover up and act as if your addiction is
really a mature or positive behavior, you run the risk of being a negative role
model. Other family members, especially young people, may join you in your
addictive behavior.

Even worse, your addiction may have cost your family money, pride, peace of mind, heartache, embarrassment, and physical pain. They may have visited you at your therapist's office, at the corner bar, at the crack house, at the hospital, in court, or in jail. You may have hit your wife, stolen from your mother, let your children go hungry, given birth to a child who has been injured by the substances you consumed while pregnant, or given your husband AIDS. As you harm yourself through addictive behavior, you can't keep the damage from spreading to those you love.

How can you hurt the ones you love and still feel good about yourself? Inside, you **know** you're acting like a selfish pig, and you may feel that your people no longer respect you. This is partly because you don't respect yourself. You may feel worthless and ashamed of your behavior.

No Choice But To Respond

> *"It got to the point we couldn't leave home because he would rob us while we were gone and use the money to buy drugs. I never thought I'd put my own son in jail but he left us no choice."*

Your out-of-control behavior will definitely disrupt your family in some way. There are a variety of ways they can choose to respond to your addiction. They may accept your behavior because they fear they will completely lose your love. They might feel responsible for what you do and just look the other way. They may rationalize your addiction as a temporary condition. Or they may actually support your addiction, fearing that if they don't you will do something worse. (See the section on **Co-Dependency** on page 17.)

Your family may also help you deny your addiction because they find it embarrassing and feel that it reflects badly on them. Parents may particularly fear criticism from their friends that they "didn't raise you right."

Whether we like it or not, we are judged partly by the company we keep. While we have choices about our friends, we don't have a choice about our family. If your family chooses not to tolerate your behavior, they open themselves to criticism of being cold and uncaring. Letting you take full responsibility for your own behavior may be the most positive, helpful, loving thing they can do, but your family may still be criticized for it. If, on the other hand, they accept, ignore, or help you maintain your behavior, they can be judged as weak, foolish, or incompetent. They are stuck in a no-win situation.

However your family and loved ones choose to respond to your addiction, they do respond. Even if they ignore your behavior, it takes energy and effort to pretend that something as obvious as addiction does not exist. It may create strain on various levels: emotional (extreme uncertainty and worry), fear (some addicts and their friends can be dangerous), social (embarrassment and rejection), financial (bills, legal and medical costs), or physical (when someone is hurt or has to take up the slack for your absence and actions). Since they are affected by what you are doing, your family members will have to deal with the situation somehow.

EFFECTS ON OTHERS

"Bobby was a born leader: first into a fight, first with the chicks, first into drugs...and first into the grave. He almost took us with him."

Besides your family, you also live in a larger social system. Some addictive behaviors are so unpleasant that friends don't want to associate with you. Loud drunks who start fights are not nice to be around. Since you spend so much time with your addiction, friends who don't share it have less and less in common with you. They drift away.

Since we all need someone, we replace our broad range of social contacts with people who are like us. As addicts, these new friends also have distorted their thinking to justify their own addictions. Therefore, they will reinforce your way of thinking that helps you feel comfortable in your addiction. Having your beliefs verified makes it easier for you to maintain your addiction — and so the cycle continues. It is not until you break this cycle that you can see how unhealthy your relationships are with these new friends.

Finally, you can trigger addiction in others. While each person must individually decide whether to perform a given act, most find it easier to follow someone else's example. Suppose you like speed because it gives you energy and helps you lose weight. You tell some of your friends, and they try it and like it, too. Then you realize that speed also leads to severe paranoia and difficulty concentrating. It's too late for you to quit easily — and too late for your friends, also.

CO-DEPENDENCY — OTHER PEOPLE AND YOU

"I thought that if I just loved and believed in him enough it could cure him."

In the life of every addict, there is usually someone who tries to "save" you from your addiction. Actually, all anyone can do for you is to save you from having to take responsibility for your addiction. Since you don't feel responsible for the results of your behavior, you are free to slide further and further into the addictive cycle.

When finally your protector's life revolves around making you well, a "co-dependent relationship" is said to exist. Although neither of you is probably aware of it, you make the other feel needed and wanted, while he or she relieves you of the need to face your addiction.

This type of relationship is both unhappy and unhealthy. The rescuer is always frustrated because he or she can't make you better — only you can do that. You, on the other hand, can't entirely ignore the problems caused by your behavior, so you blame the other person for not making things okay. After all, it's their job to "fix" you! Obviously, this relationship is way out of balance.

The person who is co-dependent will go to great lengths to make things look normal. This may mean doing your everyday chores, just to make sure they get done, or taking a second job to make ends meet. It may mean telling the kids not to bother Mommy who "has a bad headache right now," even though the children really need to talk and the "headache" is almost constant.

It may mean lying to the outside world, as in "George is too sick to come to work today," when he's really hung over. It may even mean that your "savior" will refuse to recognize what is going on so that neither of you has to face reality — for instance, believing that a sex addict was fondling a child "only to make sure the child was really getting herself clean."

This kind of behavior is called enabling. Although it appears helpful, it actually allows the addict to avoid the consequences of his or her addictive behavior. Therefore, it enables an addict to go on being addicted.

Gradually the co-dependent finds his or her identity through another person: you! They neglect their own problems, needs, and desires as they obsess on you and your situation. They focus on you instead of being their own person. You become the center of their existence, just as your addiction becomes the center of yours. Since you continue your addiction despite their efforts, their self-esteem suffers along with yours.

TIME FOR A CHANGE

While you probably don't see all of these effects in your life, some of them may sound familiar. If so, learning to control your behavior and regaining control of your life is vital. And it is possible! Even if you're well enmeshed in the cycle of addiction, it is never going to get any easier to get out. In fact, it will be easier to face yourself and start regaining control of your life **now** than it will be later on. The farther in you get, the harder it is to get out. So just how did you get in this fix, anyway?

CHAPTER THREE

NATURAL NEEDS — UNNATURAL SOLUTIONS

After looking at the patterns of addictive behavior and its effects on us and the people around us, we need to understand how *we got this way*. By knowing what forces lead us into addiction, we have the best chance to find our way out!

THE NATURE OF HUMAN NEEDS

"We're all born equal. But after that first slap, it all changes, based on what we want and what we'll do to get it."

While our lives are filled with countless desires, all humans "need" a few basic things in order to live a satisfying life. Because these needs are basic, humans have developed some basic methods for meeting them. If we are hungry, we naturally eat. If we're sleepy, we sleep. In order to feel a sense of love and belonging, we have developed relationships such as family and friendship which are common in societies around the world.

Yet people have the ability to find many different methods for meeting a need. If we try a different method and it seems to work for us, we may use it over and over until it takes the place of other methods. The method we have developed may not work as well as other methods or it may not really meet the need at all. But by the time we realize the problem, our method may have become a habit that will be hard for us to break. As we will describe in the coming chapter, this is how addictions develop.

Physical Needs

Our basic needs generally fall into three groups. Group one includes the **physical** needs for food, shelter, air, and all those things that keep us alive. Even addicts must get those needs met — although some don't do it very well — in order to survive. An addict might, for example, live in a roach-infested apartment because he gambled away the house payment. A speed freak doesn't feel hungry and thus may skip meals and become unhealthy.

Emotional Needs

The second group of needs is **emotional.** Emotional needs include love, a sense of belonging, happiness, feelings of power or control, and many others. Although we can stay alive without these needs, they are what make life enjoyable and worth living. When you're strung out you often believe that your emotional needs are being met by addictive behavior. For example, if you are addicted to it, shopping may make you feel happy, getting drunk may make you feel powerful, or getting high may make you feel free from all your problems.

But these feelings are *illusions;* you can only believe in them by wanting them to be true and by ignoring the evidence of reality.

An outside observer would see a pathetic shopper who is deep in debt and doesn't even enjoy the purchases. The observer would see a staggering drunk whose behavior is silly and laughed at by others. The observer would clearly see all the problems still surrounding the junkie who is too high to notice them. In fact, the observer would note how each one's behavior is making their problems worse rather than better! The beliefs of the addict simply do not reflect the reality seen by the onlooker.

Spiritual Needs

The third group of needs we share is **spiritual** — a need to believe that we have a purpose or that our time on earth has some special meaning. We may meet these needs through religious beliefs — such as faith in a divine being, an afterlife, or in reincarnation. Or we may hold ethical beliefs about our role in the universe — for example, belief in the brotherhood of man or in the idea that we are responsible for making the world a better place.

Whether tied to a religion or not, spiritual beliefs usually include ethical (right/wrong or good/bad) values about how we should live. In either case, we are trying to define the relationship between ourselves and the universe beyond the limits of physical reality. If our spiritual needs are not met, we may feel a sense of personal emptiness; we may feel unfulfilled, without a higher purpose for our lives.

Some people may pursue their addictive behavior in an effort to find spiritual meaning or at least as a distraction from the void in their lives. They may seek enlightenment by eating mushrooms, obtaining "perfect" sexual union, or practicing their religion obsessively. But this is somewhat rare. More often, a person who is seriously addicted lacks the time, energy, interest, or attention span required to focus on spiritual issues. He or she is simply too scattered!

When an addict does think about the meaning of life, he is likely to feel guilt for behavior that doesn't live up to his or her own code of conduct. For example, the addict may believe it is wrong to steal, but will do so anyway to support a drug habit. For that reason, addicts generally avoid facing their spiritual needs.

HOW NEEDS ARE MET

As we humans go through life, we are constantly involved in finding ways to meet our needs. Whether the need is something we require in order to survive physically or is a desire we have to make our lives satisfying and meaningful, meeting needs happens in three steps. We must:

    1) define the need or desire [label it],

    2) identify the behavior that will satisfy the need [think it through], and

    3) carry out the behavior that will satisfy the need [act on it].

This is easy to see in the physical area. For example, I may (1) *define* that funny feeling in my stomach as hunger. Then I (2) *think* about what will take care of that hunger. If I decide a bag of chips will do the trick, my (3) *action* is to find a bag and start munching.

The role of thinking is particularly important in this process. Note that the hunger did not lead directly to munching chips. What if I thought about it and decided to satisfy my hunger by suppressing it? I could choose to ignore the hunger, or I could use a drug such as speed. In this way, a natural need like hunger can be met unnaturally by a drug or starvation, rather than naturally by food. It is our **thought process** that determines how we meet our needs. It is not the need that leads to the behavior; the *thought* about the need controls our action.

The Role of Thinking

"Our life is shaped by our mind, for we become what we think."

Since our thoughts determine our actions, we have the power to take a natural need and distort it to suggest an unnatural solution. In the previous example, we could choose to satisfy hunger by eating or by using speed. If we take speed, the feeling of hunger goes away.

Since the speed took care of the hunger, obviously using speed works. Every time something works, we are more convinced it will work again. In other words, the behavior becomes reinforced. If something works long enough, we don't stop and think about what to do in a situation, we just do it. At this point, we have formed a habit.

For another example, people want to feel a sense of control over the future. Some of us decide to meet this need by buying insurance. But a gambler may decide that his or her "luck" or "system" will give her the control she needs. Thus she heads off to the track, the bingo hall, or maybe Las Vegas.

She wins! This reinforces the belief that gambling will provide the money she needs to control her future. Of course, the gambler must suppress any conflicting information (like her losses) that would suggest she is not actually meeting the need. This distortion of thinking is discussed in the section on **Denial** on page 26.

In this case, the need for control is being met only part of the time. Having a need met only part of the time is a very powerful reinforcement, however. It leads to the belief that the next time will certainly be the time that it works. In animal experiments, a pigeon who has learned to get corn by pecking at a target will continue to peck hundreds of times for a single grain. When the corn finally comes, the "fact" that pecking works is confirmed and the behavior reinforced.

Spiritual needs can also be met artificially. A man high on PCP excitedly wrote out the meaning of life and shared his list with a friend. The friend was very puzzled as she read things such as "red daffodils" and "my grandfather's bicycle." We all have a natural need to sort out the meaning of life, and this addict believed he found that meaning by using PCP. He experienced the feeling of insight and infinite wisdom, even though the insight didn't make sense when he wasn't stoned. Instead of realizing his insight was only drug-induced, he may use PCP again in his search for meaning.

Expanding the Addictive Behavior

"I was cold, lonely, hungry and broke. Then he came along and said, 'Baby, love cures all.' As long as he would be my man I thought I could live on kisses."

Once a certain behavior seems to meet a particular need, we may decide to apply it to other needs as well. Since our thought process for meeting needs was distorted in the first place, it is easy to believe that the addictive behavior will also take care of other wants. The mental process of believing that one solution can solve many problems is called ***generalization.***

For example, when the gambler sometimes wins, it has at least some connection to financial concerns. An addict who generalizes, however, begins to apply the addictive behavior to unrelated situations. The gambler might have a fight with her husband, maybe over her gambling. She then gambles to feel better about the fight, and she does feel better because she's distracted from the problem. Obviously the gambling took away the pain of the problem, but it did nothing to help solve it. In fact, it may have made things worse. However, since the behavior "worked" to help her forget her problem, she will repeat it.

The addict who used speed to control hunger may also use speed to feel more attractive, to celebrate, to get over a breakup with his girlfriend or loss of a job, and so on. As the behavior expands to more and more areas of a person's life, he or she may also begin to put the wrong label on needs. When a marijuana smoker feels bored, he may think he "needs" a bowl of pot. When faced with any kind of problem, the addict may think he or she needs the addictive behavior in order to handle it.

By generalizing that the addiction will take care of any need, the addicted person reinforces the use of addictive behavior. As that same behavior is used to meet more and more needs, the addict's life becomes more and more out of control. And the more unmanageable everything becomes, the more vulnerable we are to addictive thinking and acting. This traps us in an untamed cycle of dependency.

THE CYCLE OF ADDICTION

"My habit and I had a simple understanding: I gave it everything it wanted and it gave me nothing I needed. What a deal!"

An addiction grows because it fills an immediate urge to increase pleasure or reduce tension or pain. It takes our minds off our problems, helps us relax, and makes us feel good for a while. It may help us cover up our dissatisfaction with our lives or help us forget painful things that happened to us in the past.

As we learn that a behavior makes us feel better, even for just a brief period, we tend to repeat it. After a while, we come to depend on this behavior to help us relax, enjoy ourselves, or forget our pains and troubles. We may reinforce the pleasant effects of the behavior by thinking about it often — and not thinking about the problems that remain or any of the other things that might also give pleasure or relieve pain.

The difference between the addict and the non-addicted person is that the addict sees only part of the picture: his or her immediate need is taken care of for that fleeting moment. Addictive behavior offers temporary relief, but it will NOT solve any problems! In fact, it will cause more problems after a while. These problems, new and old, combine to create an even greater need to use the addictive behavior to "fix" things. Unresolved problems leading to quick fixes which lead to more severe unresolved problems, and so on and so on — this is called the **cycle of addiction!**

Sheer Madness

> *"Addiction is just like a merry-go-round: fun at first but it always goes in a circle, right back to where you got on."*

Obviously the addictive behavior does not "fix" anything. It only relieves, for a while, the anxiety that was created by the problem. But the problem is merely postponed; it doesn't go away at all. As we've stated, often the effort to escape results in a bigger problem than before! For example, a person may be short of rent money. This causes stress and worry. The addict may use the money he has to purchase cocaine. Using the cocaine makes him feel better temporarily. When he comes down, he has the depression that follows the cocaine high, plus he has no money for even a partial rent payment. The original problem is now worse!

As we can see by this example, addictive behaviors are not a logical response to the original problem. That is, cocaine cannot be expected to produce rent money. The addiction works on our thought process — **how we think and feel** about not having money for rent — not on the real need to pay the rent. We can use our addictive behavior to change our internal perceptions. This lets us hide from reality and forget about our problems. But reality doesn't go away and the problems keep on piling up.

Loss of Control

> *"I'm like a fireman running from one blaze to another. My whole life is consumed with damage control!"*

As the addictive behavior is applied to more and more needs, fewer and fewer real problems are faced and dealt with. The feelings about the problems are put to sleep. The pain and fear are hidden, but the problems remain. As they pile up, life becomes an uncontrolled chaos.

Very often, the addict seems unable to see any option besides the addictive behavior. The addict short of rent money may never consider negotiating for an extension with the landlord, obtaining a pay advance, or mowing a few yards for money. Instead, he will spend any money he has on more cocaine to try to forget what is really going on in his life. This will just add to his belief that he should give up because his life is hopelessly out of control. And in giving up, he surrenders his soul!

In the cycle of addiction, behavior may be performed at first because it produces good feelings. As the addiction proceeds, however, the pleasure is lost. Then the goal becomes just to avoid the pain. As one cocaine addict expressed it, "I used to get high to feel good; now I get high to not feel bad." A sex addict who molests children describes the terrible tension that comes from not carrying through on the behavior, even though the behavior causes a lot of shame and fear that bring greater pain later.

As the total burden of problems becomes too severe to ignore, the addictive behavior no longer brings the satisfaction or escape it once provided. We are then left with nothing but a tired old habit that can numb feelings, but not cover up or hope to solve life's real problems.

REAL NEEDS — REAL SOLUTIONS

"Doing heavy drugs is like swimming out to sea till you lose sight of land. You're going down for the third time before you snap that you're drowning."

Ultimately the addict can not ignore the mess his or her life has become. When these glimmers of harsh reality begin to appear, the first instinct will be to block them out by using more of the addictive behavior. But this **no longer works!** The problems have gotten too bad to be hidden any longer by the addiction. Finally the addict will be confronted with the need to find new behaviors to replace the old ones that don't work.

This is a "moment of truth." We have a real opportunity to abandon short-term, habitual responses and turn to useful solutions (see **Try A Better Way** on page 46). But too often we are so lost, tired, depressed, and overcome with shame that we try to **replace** the old, tired addiction with a new, fresh one! People tend to do this a lot in personal relationships, only to discover the same problems with a different person and place. To substitute does nothing but delay the inevitable! Take a special look at **Don't Switch Addictions** on page 45.

When you can't go on living with your addiction, you are at a *critical point.* Either you must turn around or eventually your life will hit bottom, where there is nothing left to lose but life itself. Having your choices reduced to two — living or dying — is a real eye-opener. The choice to live involves serious change and a lot of hard work. To succeed, an addict will have to start making choices based on reality, not illusion.

CHAPTER FOUR

WHY IS IT SO HARD TO CHANGE?

The previous chapters explain what addiction is and how we can get trapped by it. Now we need to understand what **keeps** *us hooked.*

CREATURES OF HABIT

"Like a stream, I followed the path of least resistance. It felt good, so I did it. Even after it started hurting, I just kept on like before."

To make life easier, all creatures develop repeated behaviors, or habits. We would be in turmoil if we had to think through every action before we did it. Many habits are positive and productive — but others are destructive and get out of control. When a behavior that we think satisfies our needs turns into a habit which we don't know how to control or stop, we have become addicted.

If we had known what was waiting for us when we took that first pill, fix, drink, kiss, or step toward our addiction, we almost certainly would not have done it. But we did it for a simple reason: it seemed to work for us. It brought us relief. It stayed with us when all the friends went away; it gave us what we thought we needed to face our world. We will *continue* to use it as long as it still seems to work.

When our addictions don't make problems go away anymore, we first try **even more** of the addictive behavior to see if that helps. This can mean pushing it right over the edge and into an early grave, mentally, physically, or both. Each of us has a different tolerance for pain and self-abuse. Only when it is clear that more of the addiction cannot possibly make things better will we begin to consider giving up the behavior. This is a very painful situation: we feel trapped, afraid, and unsure of where to turn. *Change* is the way out, but we may resist it as long as possible. Although change may be our salvation, it is usually our last resort.

We Seek Stability

Throughout history humans have clung to the things we are used to as protection against the threat of uncertainty. We resist change as if it were our lifelong enemy: each little change is like the death of something we know. In an effort to feel secure, we hold onto "the way things are," even if they are harmful or painful. The bigger the change — and the closer to home it hits — the harder we fight to stay the same.

The process of change means passing through zones of discomfort and uncertainty before we reach a new state of balance. If the change affects our deepest selves — our identity and our values — the uncertainty can be sheer anguish. For protection, we will fight against **any** suggestion that we change our inner selves.

But Change Is REALITY!

No matter how we try to keep things the same, *everything* is **always changing!** From birth to death, trying to stop change is like trying to hold back a flood with your hand. In all of life, nothing stands still. When we refuse to accept this fact of nature, we waste our energy resisting the progress we need so much. At the same time, we become suckers for anything or anyone that offers false promises of stability! We must learn how to make change work for us rather than against us! This can only happen when we accept the reality of change and develop the skills needed to grow.

The possibility of change is a bright ray of hope for all addicts! We CAN take control, we CAN improve our lives! But first we have to go through the stress of the "change process" to get there. We must learn to let change carry us toward our own best interest, rather than fight a losing battle against Mother Nature. When faced with courage, determination and skill, change can become a welcome friend rather than a dreaded enemy!

OBSTACLES TO CHANGE

Change is hard for anyone, but for an addict there are some special barriers which must be overcome before change is possible. Look at your own attitude to see how these fit you.

Denial

> *"Who? Me a junkie? That's crap!"*

For a person in active addiction, the first obstacle to change is overcoming your own **denial.** Denial is a defense mechanism, a way to keep from dealing with reality. It is a subconscious process that helps us calm our anxiety and avoid emotional conflicts. We do this by refusing to acknowledge any thoughts, feelings, needs, or events that we aren't ready to accept.

In fact, our mind tricks us by blocking out facts that we don't want to deal with. The thoughts and feelings are there — but below the surface. And it takes real effort to keep them there. The process of hiding reality from ourselves will cut us off from our true selves, distort our thinking, and make our minds less clear.

A gambler practices denial when he or she thinks only about the wins and forgets about the losses. Since he does not **acknowledge** the losses, he doesn't have to worry about the financial problems they cause for himself or his family. The problems are real, but the gambler has managed to blank this reality from his mind. A love junkie is in active denial when she refuses to see that violent melodrama is destructive, not romantic. A child molester practices denial when he or she blocks out the thought that this behavior is damaging to the child. The biggest lie you can tell yourself is that you are not addicted: not hooked on sex, drugs, golf, sweets, or whatever.

Since you deny you are addicted, you may also claim you can quit anytime. So you set up little tests. You can quit for a day or a week or a month. Some test! Any addict can do that. Maybe you've heard of the smoker who declared, "Quitting smoking is easy, I've done it hundreds of times!"

Even if you can abstain or tough it out without your addiction for awhile, you will come back to it unless you start on true recovery. Abstinence is a good start, but it never deals with the problems behind the addiction. (See the section **Recovery Is More Than Abstinence** on page 45.) Being able to quit does not mean that you're not addicted. Instead, it may help you pretend you don't need to change.

"It's no big thing; everybody in my family drinks like a fish."

Another way you may practice denial is to downplay your addiction. You may claim you're not an alcoholic because you only drink a six-pack a night, that you don't have a problem with cocaine because you only do it on weekends, or you only smoke dope after working hours.

You can always find someone whose addiction has caused more problems, lasted longer, or cost more. So what? That's like being in the hospital with a broken leg. Maybe the guy in the next bed has two broken legs, but that doesn't fix *your* leg.

In the same way, it doesn't matter whether your addiction is "better" or "worse" than someone else's. You can't measure your own problem by comparing it to anyone else's. You can only truly measure yourself by your own standards and what is happening in **your** life — without lies or excuses. You will have to admit the troubles and the losses you have suffered and the dangers you face due to your addictive behavior. Only then will you be ready to quit.

*"Man, I **have** to eat pills to put up with my crazy mother!"*

You may also deny your addiction by rationalizing: making excuses or explanations for your behavior. If someone criticizes your addictive behavior or asks you to stop, you defend your need for it or explain how it helps you. For example: "I only smoke because I'm lonely when my husband is on the road," or "I need a couple of drinks to unwind after work." You may ask other addicts to confirm that you are right and your critics are wrong.

When you've been an addict for a while, it's hard to get a handle on where you really are in your life. Your addiction has isolated you from old friends and ways of thinking. Part of your denial may be the idea that your addictive behavior has improved your life or that it's the only way to deal with an impossible situation. It may be hard for you to remember that your old life wasn't all bad — and it wasn't all great either. That's just the way life is. Still, it was better than it is now. For one thing, you didn't have to see yourself as an emotional cripple, helpless without your addiction as a crutch.

Shame

"I borrowed money from Ma to pay the rent but I scored drugs instead. Now I'm being evicted and I sure don't want to tell her."

While denial is the process of hiding the truth from ourselves, shame occurs because we don't want the world to know that we are out of control. Every time an overeater says "No, I'm NOT going to do it," then picks up the phone and orders a king-size pizza deluxe, he has a new secret to hide. As with all addictions, we are deeply afraid of our weakness being exposed to the world! When we violate our promises to ourselves and others, we have struck another blow against our self-esteem. We might as well say, "I'm weak and worthless. Why bother…just keep eating!"

This fear of exposure can be overwhelming; we will use a variety of methods to keep from being found out. We may cut other people off from us emotionally so they won't find out our secret. We may take care to stay in control of our relationships so that other people can only see what we want them to see. We may use rage as a way to distract people who might see us too clearly. Or we may become even more obsessed with our addictive behavior in order to avoid interacting with people who might find us out.

These behaviors may let us hide our compulsive habits from the world, or at least let us fool ourselves that no one knows our secret. But they cut us off from other people and destroy any chance of rewarding, intimate relationships. They also keep us from facing our problem and doing something about it!

Before we can hope to change, we have to be ready to **face** our shame, at least to the point of admitting our problem and seeking help. (Please give special attention to the section **Taking Control** on page 42). Clearly addiction keeps us enslaved by the secrecy and shame which surround it! Although difficult and painful, the results of exposure are generally not as bad as we had feared. If our addictive behavior is illegal or destructive, we may have a substantial price to pay. But even then, many addicts feel a sense of great relief when the secret finally comes out and they don't have to dread it any more.

Pride

"Anything that needs to be fixed I can do myself! I don't need to pay some fool with a Ph.D. a hundred bucks an hour to mess with my head!"

Pride is a confusing term. We are told to have pride in ourselves and our accomplishments. This is a positive kind of pride. We also can have the kind of negative pride that stands in the way of insight and change: the false pride that keeps us from admitting we have a problem and need help. Many times what seems to be pride is really denial, fear, and shame in disguise.

If we admit we have a problem, then we are free to correct it. If we aren't willing to admit we have a problem, then we have no reason to seek change. Addicts get stuck trying to pretend life is great while reality kicks us in the back of the head. What we must do is get rid of false pride. After all, no one is perfect. *Everyone* makes mistakes, gets off into traps, and has problems. When we recognize and accept that, it's not so hard to admit we are human. Then we can seek a useful solution. False pride helps keep us captive by building a wall between our problem and our ability to reach out for the help we need.

Fear

> *"So many times when my drug supply was low I'd tell myself I could quit, but then I'd get scared and score."*

Fear is the next big obstacle to change. Humans fear the unknown. Even if your present life is bad, it may seem safer than trying something new, with unknown dangers. For example, women who are being physically abused sometimes stay with the abuser instead of leaving. The abuse is at least familiar; they believe they can survive it because they have in the past. They are more afraid of the unknown problems they will face on their own.

The fear of leaving addiction is similar. Your addiction is your crutch to help you deal with life's problems. Behaviors that would really work to meet your needs are a distant memory or in some cases never have been developed at all. If you take away the crutch, you believe you will fall — that your problems will overwhelm you. The thought of facing all those problems without an escape may lead you to panic. It is terrifying to think about giving up your all-purpose solution to everything. You may not even be able to imagine your life going on without it.

You will probably also be afraid of failing if you try to quit. As long as you don't try to change, you can still tell yourself that you can stop anytime. But if you try to stop and fail, you will feel even more out of control and your self-esteem will crumble still more. It takes courage to try. It will help to remember that failure is a natural part of learning.

You will have a big void to fill if you quit. All the time you spent pursuing your addiction will have to be filled with something else. You will actually have to think about what you want to do instead of conveniently turning to your addiction. You will have to make decisions again. And then you will have to carry out your decisions, or face your disappointment in yourself for not doing your best. In other words, you will have to take control again. You will have to be responsible for your own life!

Enabling Behavior

> *"Honey, call the office for me. Tell them I'm too sick to come in — tell 'em I've got the flu. They won't ask any questions if **you** call."*

Often addicts have help from others to keep their addictions strong! When another person's actions make it easier for you to continue with your addiction, those actions are called "enabling behavior." Very often, the people who "enable" you to continue your addiction are truly concerned about you and want to help. They usually don't realize that their actions are helping your addiction rather than you.

Enabling may take the form of helping you hide the fact that you are addicted or helping you avoid the consequences of your addiction. Enabling behavior is part of a co-dependent relationship (see page 17), although not all enablers are co-dependent. For instance, your boss may let you get away with calling in sick when you're hung over. Your family may pay your bills or give you a loan when you've spent your paycheck on drugs. Your wife may accept your promise that you'll "never do it again," even though you've broken that promise 15 times already. Someone you've ripped off may feel sorry for you or not want to go to court and decide not to press charges.

The life of a co-dependent person is enmeshed with yours; other people may enable your addictive behavior for a variety of reasons. For example, your boss may overlook your absence from work just because he or she doesn't want to hire a new employee. Whether the enabling behavior is intended to help you or is done for some other reason, these actions make it possible for you to carry on with your addiction awhile longer.

Co-dependency can become a more or less comfortable habit both for you and for a co-dependent person in your life. It's handy (but deadly) to have someone else cover for you and take over responsibility for your shortcomings. It will be hard for you to start taking responsibility for yourself again.

Even when you decide to change your behavior, the co-dependent person may have trouble changing his or her role in your relationship. As you seek to change, your relationship will have to change, also. Sometimes a co-dependent relationship cannot handle recovery. The relationship may explode as one party becomes committed to breaking out of the addictive cycle.

If the people around you decide not to enable your addiction anymore, they will probably start to set some limits on their relationship with you (see **Boundaries and Limits** on page 63). It may come as a shock when your boss won't accept your excuses anymore, your family lets your car get repossessed, your wife moves out like she's been threatening all these years, or you get arrested. Even then the shock may not be enough to make you face your addiction, but without enabling behavior, it will get harder and harder for you to hide from your problems.

Physical Dependence

"After partying all night, I had to have a few toots just to get going the next morning."

If you are addicted to a substance, whether alcohol, marijuana, crack, coffee, cigarettes, or something else, you may also have a physical barrier that makes it hard to quit. After you have used the substance heavily for a long time, your body will be dependent on this chemical in order to feel normal. If you quit using the substance, your body will have an unpleasant reaction called *withdrawal symptoms.*

For some chemicals, the withdrawal symptoms are fairly mild, for example, headaches and drowsiness when withdrawing from the caffeine in coffee. With other chemicals, for instance heroin, barbituates, valium, or alcohol, the withdrawal symptoms are very severe and may even be life-threatening.

The threat of withdrawal symptoms may sound like a good reason to keep using, but look at it another way. If your body is dependent on a chemical, that chemical must have a powerful effect on your physical health. Using the chemical is generally even more dangerous than the withdrawal symptoms. If you can't handle the physical withdrawal by yourself, you can get medical help or personal support from a group such as AA or Rational Recovery to cope when the going gets rough.

Society's Obstacles

"It's Party Time!"

Even the society we live in makes it hard to give up our addictive behavior. Despite the recent publicity opposing drug use, addictive substances and addictive behavior are very popular in our culture. In fact, if all addictive behavior disappeared overnight, it is hard to imagine what our society would look like.

We think it's normal to get up in the morning groaning, "I need a cup of coffee!" Ashtrays for nicotine addicts are considered a necessary household item. Many people can't imagine a party without alcohol; they may make fun of any party-goer who asks for a soft drink. Someone who scores a bed partner at the end of a night on the town is considered more attractive than the one who goes home alone. Even illegal substances often appear in movies and on TV as glamorous, desirable, the "in thing" to do.

For kids, using addictive substances such as cigarettes, alcohol, or drugs is a way to defy their parents' rules and show that they are grown up. Young people are often ridiculed and rejected by their so-called friends for refusing to drink or smoke.

Being surrounded by addictive behavior and finding it socially accepted makes it extra hard to quit. It is much easier to give up alcohol if there is none around and the people you hang out with don't drink. People who are still addicted will encourage and even pressure you to keep using. If you make progress in recovery, it would challenge their denial that they also need to change.

Fortunately, our society is beginning to realize that addictions are dangerous and destructive. There is now much more understanding and support available for people seeking recovery from addiction. Still, in the end your decision to overcome your addiction will be made by you and carried out by you, for your own reasons.

CHAPTER FIVE

SO WHY BOTHER?

Looking at the effects and causes of addictive behavior can be a real downer. And when you add to that all the barriers to change, it can get pretty depressing. It would be easy to say, "We're trapped! It's hopeless!" But now we are going to look at the *positive benefits* of coming to grips with addiction.

REBIRTH

"If I can feel THIS bad, I can feel THIS GOOD!"

Our addictions may still give us temporary pleasure or relief from our pain and emptiness. If addiction still offers an escape route, a way to get around life's problems, why bother to quit? If we haven't developed better ways to cope, why not just go on being addicted? We know change is hard, so what the hell, why bother?

While it is true that giving up the crutch will not solve other problems, it *will* clean the cobwebs away so that solutions can be found. Recovery from addiction is "rebirth" in the true sense. It creates a new space within your life for fresh, enjoyable thoughts, feelings and activities: things that will make you feel good while you're doing them and that will leave you with positive, rewarding memories afterward.

THE REWARDS OF RECOVERY

"After two years of being clean from drugs, booze and world-class disasters, I've begun to reclaim myself. I am not a shadow any more but a real live person with the power and judgment needed to govern my future."

Having reviewed the many negative things which result from becoming caught in an addictive cycle, let's look at some of the advantages of moving into recovery. What's in it for **me**?

- *More control: the joy of true freedom!* — You can actually feel the chains crumbling bit by bit as you take more control over your thoughts and actions. Every step, no matter how small, is a major success. You learn to create your own rush without depending on some external aid or ritual. You're no longer a slave! You're free!

- *Greater self-respect* — You feel a little better about yourself each day. Guilt and shame are replaced by an ever-growing sense of pride and dignity. As your self-respect grows, **everything** else improves. Your new dignity unlocks an ever greater amount of the wonder and goodness that has been trapped inside of you. NOW you stand up straighter and look yourself and life *directly* in the eye!

- *More trust in self* — Your recovery results in a better, much more honest relationship with yourself. Each day you have a better understanding of who you are and what you stand for. You can clearly see the boundaries between yourself and the rest of the world. It's as though you become more real and solid, more stable and dependable. Now you can face and overcome things which used to break you down and leave you with a taste of sadness and disgust. You can have confidence in your decisions and in your ability to carry them out.

- *Better relations with others* — As you get more comfortable with yourself, you will also discover you're getting along with other people **much** better. Not just a narrow range of folks similar to you, but people with very different styles of living and thinking. Rather than "judge" others based on their differences from you, you begin to "accept" them based on what you both have in common! You become more tolerant, more flexible, and a **lot** more fun to be with. As we become more honest, balanced, and healthy, we attract that kind of person to us.

- *More respect for and from others* — It's neat when you recover to the point that you're not a selfish pig anymore! Addicts are one-way folks who somehow think the world and everyone in it exists to carry them around like a child. It is an important step in your recovery when you grow beyond that limited role and become the kind of person you and others most respect. At this point, you become a true adult.

- *Higher quality of life* — You just don't know how grand life can be until you begin a full-time effort to re-claim yourself from addictive thinking and acting! There is a new sense of wonder, beauty, promise. You're actually ALIVE: not a robot under the command of some brutal master. When your attention and energy are no longer consumed by an addiction, you can participate in the rich and rewarding aspects of living. You discover that everything doesn't have to be so heavy and serious; you can have fun and learn to laugh! As life continues to get better, happiness and success become your new habits.

- *Greater fulfillment* — You feel a growing sense of satisfaction in your efforts. Life is no longer just a series of problems which must be avoided or endured. The more time and energy you put into your recovery and growth, the greater your feelings of achievement. Things look and feel better! Big things, little things, everything! This is a BIG payoff for your effort and determination, all your hard work. It doesn't come all at once or hit you like lightning. It comes in little flashes of awareness, tiny glimpses of change, a sense of increased progress, achievement, and momentum.

- *More inner peace* — The tidal waves of confusion, anxiety, and frustration slowly die down and are replaced by hope, optimism, and inner calm. You don't feel like an emotional yo-yo anymore! As your stress levels decrease, you learn not to come unglued over "the small stuff." Problems come and go but you are not swept away by them as before. You have your own space now and are no longer controlled by your environment. And you begin to notice that others go crazy over the dumbest stuff — but you don't! It's wonderful to create a safe haven within yourself, a center where you can be at peace while everything around you is in crisis.

- *Increased mental balance* — Your mind is no longer a one-way street or blind detour that always leads back to addiction. Life is more than just a knee-jerk now! You won't be racing from one end of a mental see-saw to the other 24 hours a day. You discover that there is a middle point where you can stop and rest. With growing stability, you can think things through before you act and make good choices that you don't regret. You don't just react to the world, you think and choose how to respond. You refuse to let people and situations control you. As you work through recovery, you will take control **away** from the outside world and "bring it home."

- *A growing sense of unity* — It's amazing to find you're not totally isolated from the world! No longer living in secrecy, shame, and fear, the unity of life begins to appear. The weight of loneliness slips from your shoulders. A little more each day you re-join the human race, learn to share thoughts, feelings, and laughter. It's amazing to feel the natural bond that exists between all people.

- *More choices* — Recovery is the act of opening up what addiction has shut down. Everything, both within and without, continues to OPEN UP! You are not limited any more to the tiny menu of choices and feelings that come with active addiction. Every day you discover what seems to be a brand-new pocket of energy, insight, and opportunity. Living is now more exciting because your options continue to expand. It's *truly* a new day!

- *The world gets bigger* — After awhile you notice that your mental and emotional reality seems to keep growing bigger and bigger. As you feed fresh energy, hope, and power to your mind, body, and spirit, it enables you to see and feel things you were blind and insensitive to while focused on your addiction. It's like finally breaking out of your shell and being able to look around at the wonder and majesty of the universe!

- *More loving and lovable* — It is a **great** rush to give and receive love. Recovery teaches us that we can share our deeper feelings in ways that are safe and rewarding. We can come out of the isolation of addiction, build solid, real friendships, and share laughter and trust. And for the first time, the word "comfort" begins to have meaning.

- ***Better able to cope with problems*** — As you get more stable and alert, you will be able to face problems, make reasonable decisions, and follow through on them. You will always have problems and responsibilities, but now you can sort them out and do something about them. Life will still have its ups and downs, but it is no longer an unending rollercoaster of crises. And now that you are facing and solving problems as they come up, you don't have such an overwhelming burden to face each morning. You can get up with a lighter heart. Life becomes a challenge instead of a chore.

- ***More creative and productive*** — Now that you are no longer throwing yourself into a bottomless pit, you get a LOT more done because you have more time, energy, and attention. At first your life seems flat without your "fix," as though you cannot do anything unique without your crutch. But as this illusion slowly vanishes, you discover that your addiction was actually a giant dam which blocked you from applying your true power and creative resources. As your creativity flows free, you will find a greater sense of achievement.

- ***Chance for true happiness*** — "Real" happiness comes when your life is built on your **own** feelings, thoughts, and actions. While addiction gave the illusion of happiness or relief, recovery offers the real thing. It opens your mind and *understanding* to the true nature of reality. Recovery helps you take off the blinders that addiction has worked so hard to keep in place, thus allowing you to truly "see." Your world is no longer make-believe; it's built on fact, honesty and hard, hard work!

- ***Chance for spiritual growth*** — Now that you are no longer staring down into the blackness of the pit, you have the chance to look up. You begin to come into contact with the light of your spiritual nature and think on higher terms. You can explore your personal beliefs and find a way to carry them out in your daily life.

- ***A positive sense of future*** — Now there is hope! Not just some drug-induced illusion or a false expectation, but **real, achievable hope!** You can look ahead and establish goals with the confidence that there is a reasonable possibility of achieving them. Life is no longer sheer survival. You can direct your own future.

By now you know that EVERYTHING you've had to do to break out of addiction was worth it. No price can ever be too high, because the result is a life of growth and self-respect. Looking back you have only one regret: that you didn't begin sooner.

CHAPTER SIX

THE ROAD TO RECOVERY

Up to this point we've covered the nature, causes, and effects of addiction; we've examined the barriers to recovery and many positive rewards that can be achieved. Clearly addiction is not some magical force we must blindly follow. Now, we'll look at the next phase: *stepping onto the road to recovery.*

HITTING BOTTOM

"Out of dope and out of hope, I cocked the pistol, put the barrel to my head — and broke out in tears. I didn't have the courage to live and I didn't have the courage to die."

We know that change is **hard** and there are many obstacles to overcoming addictive behavior. Even the hope of a better future may not be enough to give an addicted person the motivation to change. Instead, for many people, this motivation comes from a powerful experience called "hitting bottom." This point comes when you finally get totally fed up with being a slave, when you realize that the cost of being addicted is too high to pay, when you realize that things aren't going to get any better but only worse.

"Bottom" is at different places for different people. Some reach it sooner than others, before the cost has been too great. Others don't find it until they are almost at the point of death. Until you hit bottom, the cost of quitting might seem higher than the price you pay to stay addicted.

When Is Enough Enough?

"I ate prescription drugs for 15 years. It got to where they felt like the size of a basketball in my throat and I just couldn't swallow the damn things any more. I just couldn't!"

How can you know when you have hit your bottom? Can you start your road to recovery without having to go through the horrors that others have faced, or are you just a glutton for punishment? When is enough **enough?**

Is enough when you can no longer think clearly? Maybe enough is enough when you can't get out of bed anymore, but you do to get another "fix." Is it enough when you get fired? Maybe enough is when you can't hold food in your stomach. Or after four marriages that all ended with violence and pain. Perhaps after you've been arrested or publicly labeled as a "pervert." The question is: how long will you have to stay "sick" until you get **tired...**really TOTALLY **FED UP?**

Are you tired enough yet of doubting your judgment, even your own sanity? What happened to your friends and family; do you remember seeing respect die out of their eyes? What did you do to your priorities; how far are you going to abandon your values before you call a halt?

How long are you going to be able to convince yourself that black is white and up is down? Must you face personal or financial ruin, lose everything before you snap? Have you been hit with the realization that life just wasn't meant to be lived like this?

Perhaps you really don't want to steal, lie, cheat, manipulate, or hurt those close to you anymore. Are you ready to draw a limit and say, "No more mind games, no more dope games, no more jail house games, no more cheap power games, no more silly jive — it's over!" How far do you need to push your own self-destruction?

Maybe your embarrassment is just too overwhelming when you blow it ONCE AGAIN. Maybe you just cannot continue doing things that you hate. So, what is it going to take before you get honest with yourself? When will you admit that you cannot continue to flush yourself down a toilet? Different people "reach bottom" in different ways, but you have to reach your bottom before there is hope of recovery!

The Moment of Truth

"The longer you put off facing your addiction, the deeper the hooks are set and the harder they are to remove."

As long as we can find a way to slip out of confronting our addictive enslavement, we will do so. This may be because we feel trapped in a vicious cycle with no way out — or because we're scared, lazy, or too knocked out to care. But like painting ourselves into a corner, there is less and less room to run.

Many people wake up and confront their addiction without a life-threatening crisis. But if you don't, will it be enough when the greatest loss is your will to live? How devastating it is to believe that the only way out of your mess is death. This may sound too extreme for nice middle-class addicts, but addiction has NO LIMITS. Nor does it have any regard for age, race, gender, educational level, or economic class. It will always eat as much as you will feed it. And when your hand is empty, that's OK; it will take that, too!

Somewhere, somehow, we have to stop and face the music. As the saying goes, "You can run but you cannot hide!" Sooner or later — it's only a matter of time.

Face Your Addiction

"My arms look like the B & O Railroad...and I hate to admit that I drove every spike."

It is time to confront the addiction that is creating these feelings. This will not come easy; it is something that requires effort and energy. Let's begin with the up-front facts.

First, is the realization that **you are responsible** for your own actions.

The police have yet to receive a report of cocaine forcing its way up someone's nose. And you did not surrender your heart and mind to your mate at the end of a gun. No, addiction is a direct result of a conscious choice. No matter what stresses exist in your life, you can't blame your action on anyone else, because **you** made the decision, PERIOD.

Next, you will have to admit that your dependence on an addiction to meet your needs is **a mistake.** This may hurt your pride, but you will just have to forgive yourself for being human. You can handle addiction more easily when you put it in the proper perspective — that is, "I made a judgment error," rather than "I'm a horrible person." It is hard to admit that you did this to yourself. That fact in itself is almost overwhelming. But you will have to accept responsibility before any change can occur. A sense of humor helps here. Honesty is tough, and a sense of humor is essential to get through some dark times.

Now the hardest step for any addict: you must **break through your denial** and face the truth about yourself and the world around you. Look at your addiction for what it really is: a slave master, ripping away your quality of life, your freedom. Recall who were you before you became addicted. How does that compare with who you are now? Admit to yourself that your addiction is consuming your life, inch by inch.

Now see yourself struggling, trying to find an escape — but without success. You may have struggled against your addiction before, perhaps many times, and even been successful for awhile. But in the end, the addiction overwhelmed your defenses. Recovery still seems out of reach, but at least you are moving in the right direction and that is very important!

Strength Is Required

Well-meaning folks often say that people could overcome their addictions "if they only wanted to," or "if they had the will power." These people think that overcoming addiction is simply a matter of desire. But this is not correct. It's like saying that if you hold your breath long enough, you can conquer your addiction. If you're human, you won't be able to hold your breath that long. If you are addicted, then by definition you have lost the power to control this part of your life.

Will power is not enough for the victory over addiction. What is necessary is strength and resolve! It takes great personal strength to look yourself in the eye. It is tough to face the fact that you made some major decisions which ended up hurting you and others so deeply. And it takes tremendous strength to admit that you by yourself are losing this fight. Although you may not have enough strength to win on your own, once you admit it, you can reach out for help. And with help, you can find the insight and support needed to conquer your addiction. You can do it, but you may need a lot of help from others.

Have Hope

"I didn't really care much about anything but wine and

women. When the money was gone, the chicks ran off and the wine ran out. I was in serious trouble, Jack."

When hope seems impossible and the will to live is gone, it is important to remember that there are other options available. Though you may not feel it now, the feeling of choice can return. There are many ways to get help: self-help programs, treatment centers, counselors, friends, ministers, family, and many other choices. (See **Finding the Right Help** on page 48.) The final alternative, of course, is death. This is an extreme state of mind that we hope most readers will not have to face, but for a destitute addict, that may seem the only way out. In such a condition, just knowing there are other ways to handle problems can offer that first glimmer of hope.

Hope is a vital ingredient in recovery! Addiction can rob you of hope and leave you expecting the future to be like today, if not worse. It makes you a prisoner of your "habit-of-choice." And it is all too easy for a prisoner to lose hope. So it is critical, no matter where you are, to keep your faith alive! Never lose hope in a future where you can be free of your addiction; where you can live a life of restored dignity, without shame or embarrassment. (Review the section **So Why Bother** on page 32.)

Believe that you can be in control rather than being controlled. Believe that you can direct your own life and find satisfaction for yourself. Have faith that you can meet your needs without the old crutch and feel fulfilled without slipping back into the old patterns. Recovery is hard work. These beliefs will give you encouragement and the motivation to continue on your journey.

MAKING BOTTOM

"Tired! Tired of being lost, tired of being my own worst enemy — I refuse to surrender any more of myself. That's IT, I'm done!"

Bottom Is Where You Make It

Hitting bottom helps in the recovery process because it makes you aware that this may be your last chance. You are quitting because you have finally realized the cost and the direction your addiction is taking you. You have no choice but to change or die, physically, mentally, or spiritually. This realization can give you the motivation to continue in recovery when it seems easier to give up.

But how low is bottom for **you?** How will you know when you hit it? Do you have to live the same horror stories as others who have gone before you? Or is it possible to end the insanity through your own choice? The fact is, *bottom is where you make it.*

With each individual the process will be unique. So often we hear of others who have had difficulty with the same addiction we are dealing with, and think that we have to travel the same road. While overeaters, as an example, share the problem of food intake, each person reacts differently and will be affected in his or her own way. Sex addicts, while sharing a common focus on sexual matters, are uniquely different in what they do, how they do it, and why.

There probably won't be a supernatural sign that tells you it is time to stop your destructive patterns — no voice from heaven, no message from beyond the grave. If you are looking for a light bulb to go on like in the comics, forget it. The "sign" must be *your own desire.* This is an internal event that comes as you examine your life. Maybe your body will let you know it's time to stop with some type of physical ailment, but what if it doesn't?

Too often, the obvious signs of addiction are overlooked; the wait for a "sign" ends in a solitary cell or a pine box. Take the time to reflect, to be honest with yourself and see what is really going on in your life. Honesty is the key!

Soul-Searching Time

In this critical period, you can buy yourself some time by calling time out! First, remove yourself as far as possible from the object of your addiction. Do whatever it takes. That may mean flushing your pills down the toilet, getting away from situations or people that trigger your addiction, or putting the money you need to finance your addiction where it will be hard to get your hands on it quickly. You may go to a support group meeting or even go to a hospital.

This won't "cure" you, but it will buy you a little time to begin coming to grips with your addiction. *It is very important how you use this time.* First, as we've said, you must be honest with yourself. What has addiction really done to you? What did you have before all this began? What do you really want out of life? Think about it. Better yet, write it down or tape record it. That's a start: just realizing that at one time you were able to cope without a crutch. Then look at what your addiction is doing to you: to your relationships, finances, work, play, physical health, and self-worth.

Stop making excuses for your behavior. Accept that your actions have consequences, and see what those consequences have been and where they are leading. Finally, understand that recovery is going to be costly. Not necessarily in money, but **personally.**

"There ain't no free lunch," especially in overcoming addiction. Recovery will take time, dedication, commitment, patience, energy, and effort. It will not be easy, nor quick. Recovery may mean that you will have to give up some things. Part of making bottom is being willing to pay the price, even though you don't know what price will be. You will have to decide that the value of recovery is greater than the cost and that you are ready to pay that price, *no matter how high.*

If your internal search reveals that you have sold your soul to an addiction, decide that things have gone far enough. Let the battle begin now. Draw the line and stop surrendering yourself. It's time to shine your armor, sharpen your sword, and prepare for war. This is one war you must win.

THE RIGHT MOTIVATION

"The first time I quit for Mom. The second time, for my boss.
*The third time for my girl friend. But this time it's for **me.**"*

No matter how hard they try, other people can't create bottom for you. They may mean well, but usually their message is received as nagging or preaching. By the same token, you can't create bottom for yourself just because you feel bad about what you are doing to others. It is important to realize how your addiction is affecting others, but even that is not sufficient for long-lasting recovery.

The people in quality recovery will tell you that YOU must ***want*** to recover. You must be willing to go to any length to learn how to live without your addiction. You won't hit bottom to help other people or to get them off your back. You will hit bottom when you realize your actions are self-destructive, you see what you are losing, and you've set your limits. Hit bottom because you want a better life!

Perhaps you have already tried to quit your addiction and couldn't follow through. In defeat, you wondered what you did wrong. It might be that you were doomed from the beginning because you went searching for recovery for the wrong reason. The motive to change must be *yours* and it must be **positive!** This is one time when you are standing alone, on your own two feet, as a responsible adult.

Find Yourself

If you change for someone else's reason, the type of change (if any) that you achieve might meet that other person's needs, but it won't meet yours. Even though you may act the way they want you to, you will not be you — you will just be a reflection of what someone else expects. You will lose your identity **again.** Being what someone else wants will not be satisfying in the long run. Besides, it just takes too much energy to be something you're not.

In truth, recovery is so personal, difficult, and important, it is actually quite selfish in nature. Recovery means you find your true self. You have a right to personal fulfillment. After having given yourself over to an addiction, it only stands to reason that giving yourself over to someone else will be useless. You were born to belong to you alone; any other condition is contrary to nature.

Accept Responsibility for Your Recovery

If other people motivate you to change, you don't have to accept personal responsibility for your recovery. Then if you fail, you can blame the person who forced you into recovery. This will reinforce the belief that you are not to blame for your own shortcomings. Unfortunately, this failure may also reinforce the notion that you simply can't change and may make it even harder to try again.

Recovery does not happen passively. In short, no one else can recover for you. No one can take your place and then hand you recovery. No one has ever awakened in the morning and been miraculously "cured" without any effort on their part. You must take action for yourself. You can't benefit from the actions of others.

You are the one who wants more out of life. You are the one who is dissatisfied with your life in its current condition. You are the one who is tired of being controlled. **You** want to hold your head up and not be ashamed, to feel success and accomplishment in life. You want to be able to depend on yourself and be happy with who you are. And so it is up to *you* to accept responsibility for past mistakes, as well as future successes.

Other People's Limits

There is a difference between another person setting limits for him or herself (as in, "I will not live with a compulsive gambler, exhibitionist, alcoholic, or whatever") and that person being the motivation for you to change. Another person's personal limit-setting does not "create" your motivation. You still have a choice to change or not. You may decide that **your** life is happier being in this relationship and therefore you need to change, or you may choose not to change and then accept the consequences. In either case, you act based on your **own** decision, not theirs.

That doesn't mean you should not listen to your friends and family. They may be giving very good advice or suggestions. The difference between changing for others and changing for yourself is that you listen to and evaluate the suggestions made. Then you choose those that are helpful and make sense to you. You do your own thinking and come up with your own reasons and plans for change. In other words, you get back into control and take responsibility for yourself.

TAKING CONTROL

"I've done it before and I can do it again!"

After having broken through some of the denial and accepting that recovery is a personal matter, it is time to take control of the situation and stop letting it control you. Facing addiction is not an end in itself. Simply thinking about change isn't the same as doing it! You must realize there is much work to be done.

Once you have decided to change, you will have to choose what method you will use. Again, no one can do this for you. There is much available to choose from, but the choices will have to be yours. It will be up to you to match an effective method with your good intentions. (See **Finding the Right Help** on page 48 for more information.) This will take some looking inside yourself to see how you have managed change in other circumstances. This step is important: it reminds you that you have managed change in the past. That means you can probably do it again.

You Are Only Human

Recovery will not make you a superhuman, nor do you have to be superhuman to begin recovery. In fact, denying you are human will actually slow you down. You will waste too much energy trying to hide your mistakes instead of working to fix them. It is a fact that we are "human" and therefore imperfect. We often fail or make the wrong decisions, but we are equally capable of success.

Although you have made a serious error by becoming addicted, at least the problem can be corrected. When you decide to put your energy into regaining control instead of beating up on yourself or abandoning yourself to self-pity, you can begin. Actually, you will have a lot to be proud of when you stop covering up your past and start using your energy to make positive changes in your life.

Recovery Is Hard Work

Having decided to change, you need to be realistic about how difficult this may be. Building a skyscraper single-handed is child's play compared to understanding and controlling our thoughts and feelings. To know and manage our own mind and emotions is the greatest challenge in life. You will face much hard work, painful feelings, and personal challenges on the road to recovery.

First you will face fear. Fear can keep people from trying to recover: fear of failure, fear of being alone, fear of the unknown, fear of living without your crutch. Fear cannot be denied or avoided. It must be **faced, accepted,** and **overcome.** Fortunately, once you have decided to seek help, you won't have to face your fear alone. With help, fear won't go away, but you will be able to handle it.

Failure is another human characteristic. The only way to avoid mistakes is not to try. As you fail and learn to try again, you develop greater strength and insight. Through trial and error, you can grow into your true self. Each attempt will bring you closer to success. Every effort is an opportunity for growth!

You will feel pain as part of the process of letting go. Whenever you give up something that has been a big part of your life, you will feel emotional pain. This is a grieving process, just as if there had been a death. Denying the loss, feeling angry about the loss, bargaining to keep part of the crutch or to use the crutch "once in awhile" are all part of the process. Like packrats, we don't like to get rid of anything. However, as you keep working on your recovery, you will come to accept the loss of your crutch and replace it with more positive, rewarding behaviors.

Too often we see pain as an enemy instead of a friend. During recovery, your pain will give you direction; it will point out areas where you still need to take action. It will give you proof that you're still alive and let you know that you still need to make more changes. Your pain is a sign of your growth as you work toward recovery. You don't have to "like it," but you can respect pain for the part it plays in your recovery.

Have Courage

"Actually addiction eats your faith in yourself. It's a real rush to find that you can stand up to it and win!"

It takes courage to overcome fear, failure, and pain. Courage is an individual quality. It is the ability to face and conquer something that is personally hard for you, even though doing the same thing might be easy for someone else. It is not courageous for a recreational marijuana smoker to stop using when his boss starts drug testing. It **is** courageous for an addict to face up to his or her addiction when this happens.

For most people, courage is hard to come by at first. It is present in each of us to some degree, but it takes work to develop. As you keep working toward recovery, you will get used to being courageous. Then you will find out how much easier it is to face a problem and solve it, rather than to hide it and live with the problem forever.

Last, and always very hard for a recovering addict, is the absolute need for discipline. Discipline is courage put into action; it is the rudder that steers the ship safely between the rocks. It takes discipline to stay on course and complete the journey, even through the storms. Each and every time we say "no" to a negative and "yes" to a positive, our discipline grows — and so does our commitment and strength of will.

All factors considered, recovery is tough stuff! It doesn't come easy; it will never be a piece of cake. Yet it is this very fact that makes recovery so rewarding. We can see our progress and take pride in a job well-done. The road to recovery is rocky, but along the way we find our true selves and learn to live our lives with dignity and self-respect. And since we earned these treasures for ourselves, no one can ever strip them away.

A LIFE-LONG JOURNEY

"For me 'recovery' is learning to balance my mind and actions. Not just overcoming addiction but coming to terms with myself and the world. It's a search for purpose and peace."

Recovery comes in stages, "one step at a time." Each new level brings with it some new and special hills to climb. After awhile you learn that life looks dull and discouraging when you're in the valleys but great and rewarding from the peaks.

During the low or flat times, all you can see is the burdens of the moment. The storm clouds can get very dark indeed. There will be plenty of turn-offs where the going looks easier and more inviting. At these times, it would be all too easy to fall back into old ways and habits.

This is when courage is critical and self-discipline must carry you through. You can mentally "record" and cherish the fresh energy and the wonder you feel when you take a step forward. To help you through the low times, you can "re-live" within yourself the rush of pride you get from keeping yourself clean and coming such a long way.

Don't Switch Addictions

"Gave up drinking and got into smoking dope. Kicked grass but began to over eat. Got the food under control but am strung out on jogging. Hell, I bet I'm the healthiest addict in town."

In the recovery process it is very tempting to switch one addiction for another and give yourself credit for "being cured." It is not uncommon for alcoholics to begin a marijuana maintenance program, or rage-a-holics to start binge eating. Some people may even become addicted to their recovery program. Then, in a false feeling of success, they push out their chests and declare that they have overcome their original addiction.

In order to overcome addictive behavior, it is not just your particular addiction that you have to give up. You must give up addictive behavior in general! If you switch to some new escape, you are still a slave to something you can't control. If you believe this has cured you, you have just found another form of self-deception or denial — a sidetrack away from the road to recovery. Your ultimate goal must be to go from dependence to **independence.**

Recovery Is More Than Abstinence

"People are like emotional Swiss cheese; everyone has holes, just in different places and sizes. If you don't heal your wounds, you just keep trying to fill the same old holes with new things."

So if you give up your addictive behavior — you don't use the substance or act out the behavior — does this mean you're cured? Is abstinence all there is to recovery? Some folks think so. If that's it, what is all the fuss about? Just stop whatever it is you're doing and you've recovered! Then why do so many people keep going to recovery meetings and claim that they are recovering but not cured? Why do we see recovering addicts who cannot sit through a meeting without going out to have a cup of coffee, loaded with sugar, or a quick smoke?

Recovery is more than abstinence, holding back from the addictive behavior. Avoiding the addiction is good, but it is only the beginning, not the end. Restraint is just the first step on the road.

People who stop their recovery at abstinence make life miserable for themselves and those around them. They may constantly complain about their sacrifice. Or they may get to be pests because they are always seeking compliments for avoiding their addiction. If they try to abstain by using their will power, their lives will be a constant struggle; any second of relaxation may give the addiction a chance to overtake them again. Without deeper changes in their lives, they may stop using their addictive behavior, but they won't be able to stay stopped with comfort. Abstinence can be an unending struggle, with no progress, no rewards, and no end in sight.

Recovery requires that you **deal with** the needs that your addiction was supposed to fulfill. All those issues that you have carried around but not faced are still out there waiting to be resolved. Until you face them, you will have to find some way to hide them from yourself. And this leads to more unnatural solutions, more addictive behavior. Recovery means facing your unresolved issues and working through them.

Lure of Forbidden Fruit

> *"It's a hunger that begins to crawl up your spine, a silent scream for that RUSH!"*

Situations will always come up that will make it be easy to fall back into old patterns. To avoid this trap, you will have to find a different direction for your life. Work to fill your life with positives to the point where addictive behavior won't have room to thrive. It will **not** be easy to do this. You will need help to get started and to maintain your momentum. Success often turns on finding the right help at the right time.

Recovery then becomes a lengthy journey. As we face and resolve one issue, another will arise to be dealt with. Our behavior is rooted in our thoughts and our thoughts are built on how we see ourselves and the world we live in. We will run headlong into our old self-defeating thought patterns (review **How to Think Like an Addict** on page 5). It is not just a matter of regaining control over one piece of our lives. We must change the way we think about ourselves and the world. This will bring some balance and sanity to our existence as a whole.

Although this process sounds overwhelming, this is what life is all about. Recovery is no mystical cure or medical remedy that can only come as a gift from God or the skills of a therapist. It is a path, slow and increasingly certain, which can lead you into a healthy, balanced way to live your life with fullness and joy. You don't have to wait for the end of the path to enjoy what you have achieved. The rewards for your efforts will come to you along the way. After awhile, you quit worrying about the goal and start enjoying the journey.

Try A Better Way

> *"Positive intent + the right help + fresh thinking + sincere effort + reasonable time = a New You."*

For some reason we think we can do the same old things as before and get different results. If you're typical, you have "quit" several times. You may have switched addictions or you may have abstained completely for a while. You have not, however, remained addiction-free. So now is the time to move on from the old ways of doing things. If the old methods didn't work before, they probably won't be any better this time. But don't give up: try a different technique.

Now is the time to try a change. Recovery is a process and there are points in that process where outside help is needed. Recovery requires that you stop the addictive behavior, of course, but also that you address the problems that led you into addiction in the first place. You need to analyze the way you respond to your internal needs and to outside events, then learn new ways to respond.

It is this part of recovery that calls for outside help. And the help will be most effective if you get it on a regular, on-going basis. It is as if you are looking in a mirror. You can only see the reflection of the part of you that's facing the mirror. To get a complete picture you need to use more than one mirror. Likewise, it is impossible to see ourselves completely without feedback from others. Getting help will give you a system of checks and balances so that you can tell if what you are doing is healthy for you. If you are going to change your behavior, you need this mirror.

CHAPTER SEVEN

FINDING THE RIGHT HELP

OK, we have considered what addiction is, how it commands us, why it is hard to change, the rewards of recovery, and the turning point toward change. Now we get down to business! To continue into recovery and turn your ambitions into reality, you will have to *find the right help.*

REJOINING THE HUMAN RACE

"I'd lock myself in my trailer house for weeks at a time. Just me, my dogs, my drugs and my pistol. I didn't want to see anybody but my connection and the Good Humor Man."

An addiction will keep us alone and set apart. There are **lots** of ways people become isolated. Perhaps you grew up in a family which never showed its feelings. Many times people close up due to extreme abuses in their past. Or maybe you've spent a lot of time in the streets and your experiences have "hardened your heart." Convicts and ex-cons fresh out of prison often fall off into this trap.

The denial, fear, false pride, depression, hopelessness, and shame that keep us trapped in addiction also cut us off from other people and the world around us. We do everything possible to ignore, disclaim, or hide our addiction from view. Our egos tell us our problems are so unique that "no one could really understand," plus "nobody gives a damn anyway," so why bother?

This "prison of self-isolation" is deadly. We have cut off our communication with the world, except for those people who share or support our addiction. In fact, we have built an invisible cage that we carry around with us. As long as we are trapped inside, we can be easily confused and controlled by our addiction. We are not free to reach out for fresh insights, a dose of reality, or for the help we need to release ourselves and fight the addiction.

Recovery Means Reaching Out

It is *never* easy to share our thoughts and feelings, even under the best of conditions. And the more personal the issues involved, the more fearful we are of being vulnerable and abused. This is especially true with our addiction concerns because they involve *very* personal issues: things we don't want to look at ourselves, much less let anyone else see. And when our addiction involves a behavior defined by society as illegal or immoral, it makes the situation even worse!

From inside the cage of isolation, it may seem impossible to reach out for help or to let anyone see inside. However, this attitude is part of the trap we are caught in, just one more way that our addiction deceives us. Now that we have admitted we have a problem with addictive behavior, we must recognize that we need help to overcome it. If we continue to grasp our addiction to ourselves in secret, it will pick our bones dry.

To break the cycle of addiction, we **must** break out of our internal prison and establish contact with the world again, especially with those who can help with our recovery. So our very first step into recovery is to find a safe and sensible way to come out from under our rock. This will certainly feel risky and uncomfortable, but it will grant a much-needed sense of relief. It is this willingness to come out into the open which enables future growth!

PREPARING YOURSELF

"Traveling into the unknown is tough without a map. It must have been a real problem for Columbus, too."

Alone in your cage, you may tell yourself that no one is smart enough, safe enough, or hip enough to help you break the cycle of addiction. But this simply isn't true. In fact, much of what you think, feel, and do under the influence of addiction is **clearly understood by others.** It follows a pattern that many people have experienced before your addiction ever took hold.

Today, there are lots of capable people who have insight, experience, and training in addiction problems. They can recognize what you are going through and help you confront and overcome your addictive behavior. If you look, you can find a group, a counselor, or a program that offers the skill and concern you need.

A Price To Be Paid

"More than time, more than money, recovery requires that you learn to love and respect yourself — perhaps for the first time."

Once you make the critical decision to get help, you must prepare yourself to go in with an open mind. Because you have been addicted, your thinking will be distorted for awhile even if you have stopped practicing the addiction. Your thoughts and feelings may be very confused right now, so focus at first on your **actions.**

Make your life as simple as you possibly can. You are in for a major struggle and you don't need any unnecessary complications. Avoid the "friends" who shared your addiction with you. They can only lead you back down the old road to slavery. If any of them are truly your friends, they will find you and be glad to share your new life and interests.

Remember the first reality of recovery: from start to finish, your progress is **your responsibility. YOURS!** Not your mother's, not your counselor's, not some judge's. Only by accepting this responsibility can you achieve the pride, dignity, power, and control that come with recovery. We suggest you memorize the following thought and use it often: **"The benefits come to the one who pays the price."**

Having come to terms with this concept, you are now ready to enter the demanding and rewarding world of personal recovery and life-long growth.

Clearly it helps to know what to expect, both from yourself and others. The practical information in the rest of this section is intended as a guide to finding help.

Attitude is EVERYTHING

"In treatment, more than any other time, you get what you give. No more, no less."

The ideal reason to go into recovery is because you want to have more control and **live a better life.** But, let's face it, that is a "healthy" attitude that many active addicts will not share. In fact many people seek help with their addictions just to get the "monkey off their backs." They are sick and tired of being sick and tired, but they haven't looked ahead to the rewards of recovery. Others find themselves in counseling because it is required as a condition of a court sentence. Some go because their family or an employer has "laid down the law."

Whatever your reason for going, just attending sessions or showing up "because you have to" does not guarantee a "cure." The best counselor in the world cannot help you if you aren't willing to contribute to your own rehabilitation. If you go as a rebel or determined that nothing will happen, that is *exactly* what will happen: nothing. You get what you put into it.

Any progress toward recovery will be based on your desire, steady participation, and cooperation in the process. This is a trip that begins and ends within you! You must find your own reason for overcoming addiction and be ready to put out **serious effort** to get free of it. Breaking out of addiction is a major challenge; it must become your **number one priority.** Anything less than **total commitment** won't cut it! Frankly, many people are not willing to pay this price. They would rather live and die a slave than face the problem and fight back.

Under Supervision?

"They took my name, gave me a number and threw me in with a herd of gorillas. I knew right away I wasn't going to like the place."

If you are under correctional supervision (prison, probation, or parole), you may be required to participate in some type of treatment. Clearly no one wants to have something forced down his or her throat. If you go because you "have to" or you think it will improve your legal situation, it is unlikely that you will make any meaningful change because you are in a closed state of mind.

But if you are going to participate, even against your will, it makes sense at least to use the opportunity to listen and learn. Perhaps you will come to a point where you want to change rather than stay under the influence of an addiction that endangers your physical and mental freedom. Please take another look at the section on **The Right Motivation** on page 41.

If, in fact, you do not want to be in treatment, think about this: the criminal justice system can take our physical freedom, but addiction can and does take much more! It can take our very will to live and enslave us FAR beyond the capacity of some judge! And, just for the record, many people who return to jail and prison do so because they return to their addiction. So if you have a chance to come to terms with your dependencies, it is in your best interest to do so. And that is a cold-blooded fact!

What's Out There

"Before you write the world off as useless, take a GOOD look around. You never know what's out there until you really check it out!"

Depending on your situation, you may have a lot of choices in the type of "help" you get, or you may have none. If you're locked up or stone broke, you don't have choices; you take what you can get! When you do have a choice, think about what kind of treatment program or counselor would be best for you before you jump into the first program you find. This is an important decision because it will affect a very private, sensitive part of your life.

Many communities have an information and referral service listed in the phone book; this service can tell you about the government and nonprofit treatment programs in your area. You can also call the local government offices and look in the Help Pages and Yellow Pages of the phone book for the names of treatment programs and counselors. Mental health and drug treatment agencies, and even hospitals, usually know who and what's available. Or if you begin by going to a self-help group, many of the members will have first-hand experience with who's who. Your doctor, minister, or even a friend who has mastered his or her own addictions also might provide some names of programs or counselors.

Even when you are "required" to participate in treatment, you should check things out and make input into the type of counseling that you think will be most helpful. There are many options. In-patient or out-patient? Group or individual? Professionally directed (psychiatrist, psychologist, licensed professional counselor, certified drug and alcohol counselor, for example) or self-help group (NA, AA, RR, etc.)?

In-patient treatment may be necessary if you expect to have severe withdrawal symptoms and need medical help called detoxification to get chemicals out of your system. You may also need in-patient treatment if your life is so messed up that you need to get away from your environment so you can concentrate on making a major change in your life. However, in-patient treatment is usually more expensive; when there are low-cost programs available, there may be a long waiting list. **Out-patient** treatment is best when your life is at least somewhat stable and you have enough discipline and support to help you maintain your recovery in between meetings. Both types of programs should provide for long-term follow-up. Addiction is a very deep-seated problem. It doesn't disappear overnight, in ten weeks, or maybe even in a few years.

Different Strokes

"No one way is right for everyone. A big part of success is making the right match between you and what best moves you from addiction toward freedom."

There is a difference between counseling that takes place on a one-to-one basis and in a group. There is not one "best" program that meets every need; each has its strong points. **Individual** counseling is more private, usually more expensive, and may give you more time to focus on your deepest problems. It may help you come out of your isolation gradually, since you can share your problems with just one person at first. Individual counseling may also be more comfortable when you are working on issues that are extremely sensitive and hard for you to face.

Groups are excellent to draw you out of your isolation. They help you see that you "are not alone" and let you share experiences with people who have been where you are now. Other group members are there to lend you strength when yours has run out.

There is no fixed rule as to whether you should begin with individual or group counseling. Some people find a balance by being involved in both at once or at different times. Mixing the two kinds of therapy can be very effective.

There are two very different types of groups. One kind of group is the "self-help" group which is described in the next section, **Self-Help Groups and You.** Groups of the other type are organized, limited to members who have been accepted into the program, and are guided by a professional counselor. The members are usually at a somewhat common place in their recovery and work with the counselor to help each other. The group may meet for a fixed number of sessions and may have a definite treatment plan or list of issues to be dealt with. These groups are usually very serious about confronting the problems behind the addictive behavior. They may have expected outcomes and work to move the members on to the next level of recovery.

Regardless of the type of treatment you enter, remember that it will affect the quality of your life and the course of your future. Make a commitment to yourself to seek **long-term recovery from addictive behavior,** not just abstinence from a particular substance or action. This approach will give you the greatest rewards throughout your lifetime.

Self-Help Groups and YOU

Many people choose a self-help group to guide and support them on the road to recovery. These groups are much looser and more informal than the structured groups led by a professional counselor. All are groups of people with addictions who meet to seek recovery. Members come and go, often there is no fixed "leader," and the focus of the discussion is picked by the people attending the meeting. Self-help groups vary depending on the commitment and leadership of their members. Some are more a "social sharing" than a formal treatment activity. Because the group is informal, it may not push its members past their comfort level. While this makes the meetings more serene, it doesn't offer the greatest potential for growth and recovery. Some self-help programs are more serious than others about working toward in-depth recovery rather than mere day-to-day abstinence.

Twelve Step Programs

"Keep coming back!"

The first self-help group that many addicts turn to is a Twelve Step program, for example Alcoholics Anonymous, Narcotics Anonymous, and Overeaters Anonymous. There are other anonymous groups for sex addicts, gamblers, love addicts, and so on. Whatever the addiction, the principles and steps are similar.

Twelve Step programs get a special mention here because they have worked for thousands of people. The programs are free and are available almost anywhere, almost anytime, now and whenever they are needed. They offer understanding and hope because you can see other members who have been through addiction and are working toward recovery. Through the support of other members, they offer strength to help you get through another day or another crisis *without* kicking back into your addiction.

The Twelve Step program is based on a series of 12 actions which you take over a period of time to stop your addictive behavior and heal. As you "work through the steps," you may choose a "sponsor" who has gone through the steps and can offer you guidance and support. As with any type of recovery, you must be honest, committed, and open-minded before you can make progress. You must participate **actively:** you cannot expect more out of the program than you put in.

If you decide to attend a Twelve Step program, you will find that many different types of people attend meetings, from rich to poor, skilled to uneducated. Be ready to try several different groups until you find one where you feel comfortable with the people. This is not the same as feeling comfortable about your addiction; that type of discomfort is part of the denial process.

Some group members will be more committed to recovery than others. Some are there just to meet probation, prison or parole requirements, to socialize, or for some mind-game of their own. If you hang out with them, or if that's the only reason you are there, you will **not** make progress in your recovery. It's up to you to pick out the people who are serious about recovery and work with them.

At first all of your efforts will be focused on not using your addictive behavior. After you've been free of your addiction for some time (usually three to six months), you will be better prepared to face some of the problems and pain that were hiding behind your addiction. You need to learn better ways of thinking and coping and ways to improve your relationships with yourself and other people. At this point, it may help to see a private counselor to work through the deeper issues that drive your addictive thoughts and actions.

Be careful to avoid switching to a different addiction or actually becoming addicted to your recovery program! As you progress, you will begin to find inner peace and restored power and dignity. Although you may still go to meetings, the struggle against addiction should not be the focus of your life. Work instead toward your future growth and achievement.

What To Look For

Having checked out what is available, narrow your list to two or three possibilities and call each. Counselors and programs should be competent, familiar with current treatments, and have experience in working with addictions. Self-help groups should respond to your call and show concern and support for your participation. Although we all have a lot in common when it comes to addictive behavior and underlying problems, each addiction has its own unique aspects. Therefore, it is helpful for the program or counselor to have experience working with your special type of addiction.

If you aren't sure about a group, person or agency, **ask** about their background, training, and qualifications. They should be willing to provide the names of other professionals or agencies who know their work. They are not going to provide the names of former patients, however, as this would violate confidentiality.

When you talk to a counselor, you should be able to sense a sincere and caring attitude. This doesn't mean everything has to be "warm and fuzzy" but you do need to feel like an individual, not just another case. Since addictive behavior can overwhelm you suddenly, it is usually important that the counselor or group will be available if you are feeling weak. When this isn't possible (counselors also get sick, visit relatives out of town, etc., and cannot always be present), he or she should be prepared to give you the name of some other person or facility to call in case of emergency. If you are under correctional supervision, it will make it easier for you if your counselor has an understanding of the requirements of your supervision.

If you are considering group counseling, ask about the size of the group; anything above 12 may be too big to provide much individual attention. If it is individual counseling, ask how long and how often you would meet. While the length of the treatment cannot be guaranteed, you should ask what is the average length of treatment.

You will also need to ask about the practical aspects of the program, such as location, costs, payment plans, sliding fee scales, time commitments, and so on. You will need to make sure that the program is really practical for you. If you don't have transportation, is it on a bus route? If you are working 8 to 5, does the program offer evening or weekend sessions? Make sure you understand the payment arrangements in advance. Also ask the counselor or program to explain any commitments they require, such as an agreement not to miss any sessions, to remain in treatment for so many months, the involvement of your family, or a requirement that you pay for a session even if you don't go. A reputable counselor or program will not be offended by these questions.

How to Choose

"No one way is 'right' for everyone. Choose what works for you! If that doesn't do it, take what you've learned and try again — just keep trying and it will come."

Again, if your treatment is required by the court, such as for probation or parole supervision or in a jail or prison rehabilitation program, your choice of treatment is limited or you may not have any choice at all. You may be simply "assigned" and have to make the best of it. In this case, do your very best to walk in with an open mind. Don't let the fact you "have to be there" do you in.

If you are on probation or parole and do have some limited options, you can help by stating your preferences, if you have some, and explain your reasons for your wishes. Your officer may know what's locally available and best suited to help you start in the right direction.

Naturally when you are free to choose, you will feel much more in control. You have the opportunity to deal with who you wish and are clearly involved because you want to be. However, you will have to take the initiative to find help and get started in treatment.

Getting started can be tough if you don't have any money. Some people are lucky and have insurance, but even this is limited and doesn't pay the whole cost. Many insurance policies will pay no more than half of the cost, are limited to a low hourly rate, or they may cover only in-patient treatment or only certain types of therapists. If you don't have insurance, you should look for programs that set their fees based on your ability to pay. Many agencies and individual counselors charge on a "sliding scale" or will work out a payment plan with you.

If you can't afford even these lower rates, you may be able to find a government program or a nonprofit agency that offers free treatment. Since there are many people who can't afford treatment, there will very likely be a waiting list for these programs.

You may decide to seek out a self-help group. These are usually free and generally offer sincere understanding and down-to-earth support for your efforts to remain addiction-free. A self-help group can also offer you support while you're waiting to get into a program, as follow-up after you have completed other treatment programs, and additional insight while you are getting other treatment.

Give It a Fair Try

When you have made your choice, be prepared to give the program you select an honest try. Three to eight sessions are generally recommended for this. The effort to change can be pretty scary, and it takes time to develop trust in a group or a counselor.

As you start out in treatment, a word of caution. One of the oldest tricks in the book is to avoid looking at and dealing with yourself by shifting the focus to someone else. If you're still grasping for ways to avoid dealing with your addiction, an easy one is to focus on the shortcomings of the people around you. Maybe they have an eating problem, low intelligence, or otherwise just don't fit the bill as a model human being. So what?

You aren't there to judge your counselor or the group! It's time to look at YOURSELF. Don't expect your counselor or other group members to be "perfect" before they can help you help yourself. What you are looking for in a counselor is his or her **insight** and **skill.** Counselors don't need to be heroes or superstars. They just need to know more than you do and be able to share their knowledge with you as they guide you toward recovery.

YOU AND YOUR COUNSELOR

If you choose to get individual or structured group counseling, you will still have a choice as to the counselor you see. Just as one form of treatment works for some and not others, so the same counselor is not right for everyone. While you need a therapist that you can respect, and who you believe has the potential to help you, you do not have to have a person you might pick as a best friend. In fact, a counselor is not your personal friend in the usual sense. A certain distance must be maintained in this type of relationship and you should not expect to socialize outside of the counseling session.

What To Expect

All in all, counseling is a relationship between two humans. Counselors have developed special skills and techniques to guide others in finding solutions for themselves. They do not have special powers, magic wands, or crystal balls. They cannot force you to change or change for you; they can only guide and encourage you. It will be up to you to accept responsibility and take the steps necessary to recover. This change occurs through a mutually respectful relationship. Just as the addiction was yours, so then is the recovery truly yours. Although you may feel very lost and low as you start recovery, you have the seeds within you of a strong, competent, vibrant human being.

Besides knowing that you need to cooperate and work at your recovery, you also need to know what to expect. First, let it be clear that you will not be well and healthy after two or three magical sessions. Addiction is like an old tree with very deep roots. Recovery takes time; it is not a quick fix! In most cases, years of gradual growth are involved.

Again, the most important factor in the success of your recovery is YOU. The next factor is your counselor's skill and the quality of your relationship with him or her. Counseling is a very rare and special exchange of energy and trust. Its purpose is *growth*.

Your Counselor's Job

"The dude was like an old buffalo hunter...he could read the signs."

So what does this "professional" do that you cannot do for yourself? First of all he or she is *objective.* While most of your choices are subjective, or emotional, your counselor will be able to see your behavior and choices from a more logical and rational view. The counselor's view of you and the world is not confused or clouded by your addiction. Thus you can test your view of reality with someone not under the control of addictive thinking. The counselor is able to encourage new ways of thinking and acting that will be in your best interest, rather than those addictive acts that are most convenient for you.

The counselor is actually a *trained guide* who will help you discover and use your own strengths to solve problems. He or she will ask questions, discuss options, ask you to reflect on what might work for you, and reinforce your achievements as you make progress. He or she may suggest "homework" to help you find success in new ways of coping. Remember that addictive thinking often displays itself in many parts of our lives as a way to deal with our problems. Therefore you will need to develop new and more effective ways to solve problems in several areas of your life.

A good counselor will recognize that you are unique and must follow what works for you. He or she will **not make judgments,** but will focus instead on helping you see that you are a worthy person even though you may engage in negative behaviors at times, as we all do. The realization that you are a worthwhile person will often help you immensely in building the self-esteem necessary to resist your addiction or stick with your recovery.

Last, a good counselor will **not tell you how to live your life.** He or she may help you think about the consequences of some of your choices and ask you to decide whether the results are desirable for you. In this way, you grow to discover the cure within you.

Your Contribution

"He told me right up front: 'There ain't no free lunch'."

So what do you bring to a counseling relationship? **Honesty** and **sincerity** are the most important qualities you can bring. In the initial sessions it is okay to state that you are not yet comfortable discussing a certain subject. Trust comes with time and isn't expected right away. However, if you are not willing to be honest after trust is established, you cannot expect much progress.

The second quality you must be willing to develop is **an open mind** so you will try to put into practice the behaviors that seem likely to aid your recovery. Change is not easy for anyone; we all fear failure and the unknown. So **commitment** is required, along with **courage** and **determination.**

Also, because addiction has been growing for a long time, **patience** is absolutely essential! You didn't get the way you are overnight and you won't get addiction off your back by wishing it away. You need to be willing to make gradual, agreed-upon changes. You will have to evaluate the results of these changes and then decide what is most productive for you.

Confidentiality

A special word is needed about **confidentiality** (privacy). It goes without saying that you do not want a blabber mouth for a counselor. However, if you are required by law to be in treatment, it may be necessary for the counselor to report your attendance at sessions and give *general* statements about your progress.

It is very important that you have a clear understanding about the counselor's obligation to report any current drug usage or criminal activity to the courts. The counselor will generally not report specific details back to the criminal justice system, as this disclosure would prevent the client from discussing their addiction honestly. However, the laws about confidentiality are very complex and different in different locations. To prevent misunderstanding later, make sure you discuss the issue of confidentiality during the first session with your counselor. If you are under correctional supervision, you should also ask your correctional officer to explain what information is confidential and how much of your treatment can be disclosed.

Communication with all other persons should not occur without your written consent or under court order. This means that your friends or family cannot get information, no matter how much they are trying to help, without your permission. This sometimes offends concerned family members. You can help by explaining the counselor's obligation not to discuss your case with anyone.

STAGES OF TREATMENT

The Moment of Truth

> *"Coming to grips with myself, facing the truth of it all, was the hardest thing I've ever had to do...and I didn't like it! "*

There are several basic stages in the early part of a counseling relationship. The first is an *introductory* stage where you get to know your therapist and he or she gets to know you. There may be formal or informal assessments in the first several sessions. It is likely that you will not totally trust your counselor at this point. But if you have strong negative feelings about a counselor, this may not be the right person for you.

Just be honest with yourself about the real reason you are dissatisfied. Where's the problem? Do an "attitude check": Is there a *real* barrier between you and the counselor *or* are you transferring your discomfort with change into dislike of the change agent? It's not necessary to "like" your counselor, but it is necessary to be able to respect him or her and to learn through their guidance.

As therapy proceeds, it is almost certain there will be some confrontation with your counselor. He or she will challenge your defenses of your addiction, your attitudes, and the resulting behaviors. Counselors frequently hear excuses for why a client continues the addictive behavior, statements that the client is not really addicted, and explanations that the addictive behavior is helpful or necessary to the client in some way. A good counselor will dispute these statements: don't take it personally. This stage involves the breaking of denial about the addiction. It is absolutely essential in order to achieve success.

You must expect that there will be serious conflict during this stage! It is not a good time to run off or demand a new counselor if you were comfortable before this phase. There will naturally be a difference in the way you see the world as opposed to the way the counselor does. THIS IS WHY YOU ARE SEEKING RECOVERY! It is **not** the counselor's job to tell you what you want to hear. You go into recovery to learn the difference between illusion and truth: not what you'd like to be true, but the way things really are. **Beware:** don't let your fear of facing yourself or your addiction sabotage your chances of success! Give things a chance to settle down and work before you just bail out.

Your counselor may also want you to participate in a self-help group such as a Twelve Step program. The group can help you break through your denial, give you support, and offer a place to go when you are having trouble staying away from your addictive behavior. In general, counselors see Twelve Step and similar groups as working toward the same goals as counseling and therefore helpful to your therapy.

Sticking With It

"Say, man, I'm fixed! And I'm outta here!"

As your recovery proceeds and you are not engaging in your addictive behavior, there will be a temptation to declare yourself cured and leave treatment. Do not be surprised if your counselor disagrees and is not ready to release you! Remember, most people achieve periods of abstinence for some time without recovery. There is often an initial period of success which is followed by over-confidence and failure to keep on working at recovery.

As your program progresses, there will be less and less discussion about your addiction and more and more about the way you manage life in general. In an advanced state of recovery, you begin to learn new ways to deal with "truth" and "reality." This is the process of *rearranging your thinking.* Earlier in the book we talked about how addicts typically think, for example, all or nothing, needing it all now, etc. The fact is that not **thinking** like an addict goes a long way in not being an addict!

Another phase of treatment may involve *learning skills* necessary to solve the problems you thought were unmanageable. You may learn to budget to prevent huge financial pressures, learn organizational skills to prevent undue time pressures, or learn how to set and evaluate realistic goals to prevent constant feelings of failure. These are just a few examples of the many types of skills that can be taught.

Another aspect of treatment usually is *education.* Understanding addiction and your addiction in particular aids in controlling it. It is similar to understanding how your car runs. The more you understand, the more likely you are to be able to keep it running. By itself, however, just the "understanding" of a car or an addiction does not assure success in keeping the car running or the addiction under control. All the understanding in the world does not keep a car going without fuel. Likewise, just understanding an addiction will not cure it if behavior does not change. Therefore, **your actual behavior** is the test of your recovery!

There is no set time for each of these stages and moving back and forth between stages is not uncommon. The time required to achieve a good result is influenced by motivation, determination, degree and reason for addiction, and family and peer support, among other factors.

You must remember that you are a unique individual whose recovery cannot be compared to someone else's. Recovery is an ongoing process, but it gets less time-consuming and far more rewarding as time goes by.

PROGRESS!

"The only way I know how to put it is that now I can see things coming before they get here and they don't kick my butt like they used to. It's neat!"

After you have gotten comfortable without your addictive behavior and begun to face the problems hidden by the addiction, you will notice a difference in the ways you think and act. Many of the extreme attitudes described in **How To Think Like an Addict** on page 5 will begin to shift. Your life will slowly take on **balance,** resulting in a lot more control over how you react to daily life. And as you learn more positive ways to direct your thoughts, feelings, and actions, the influence of addictive control will gradually slip away.

The resulting sense of progress and achievement is a wonderful experience! All the sweat and pain seem worth it when you feel your life growing forward. By now much of the discomfort of recovery is over because you are working for yourself rather than against yourself. You're not beating your head against a wall any more trying to hold onto the past. As you flush the past, you have more and more room for new, fresh thoughts and feelings. You become very encouraged: you clearly see that your progress gets faster as you build more skills and stability.

If you have been going to a self-help group only, you may decide to cut back on meetings or not attend regularly. If in counseling, you and your counselor will finally agree that you have substantially completed treatment and are ready for discharge. You have learned to recognize triggers in yourself that lead you to engage in your addictive behavior. You have examined and rearranged your thought patterns. You have learned to control your impulses and have developed appropriate coping strategies when pressures come up. You have not engaged in addictive behavior for a significant period of time.

Now you are ready to go try your wings. However, follow up and support are **very important.** If you are in counseling, your counselor will probably recommend checkup appointments to reinforce your more productive way of life. He or she will remind you to avoid old thought patterns, coping strategies, and associations as a way to prevent a relapse into your addictive behavior.

You will also review the resources you can call on to help you manage in the future when you may feel weak or relapse is more likely (see the next section on **Backsliding**). You may want to join a follow-up group if one is available or keep going to meetings of your self-help group.

You can use your extra time to do something positive with your life, for example, learn a new skill, develop a new talent or hobby, spend more time with your family or church, or contribute to the people around you through volunteer work. Always remember your group or counselor will be available if you need help with problems or feel yourself slipping.

Backsliding

> *"One day a little voice will say, 'You're on top of it now, just one joint wouldn't bother you'. Man, you must NEVER forget that your addiction is a liar!"*

Your challenge now is to remain addiction-free. You need to realize that you will always be vulnerable to addictive behavior and thought patterns. You are just like the patient who has had back surgery. You are in good shape now, but you need to take care of yourself and avoid situations that might lead back to addiction.

To avoid a relapse, you must take good care of yourself, mentally, physically, emotionally, and spiritually. Stay in touch with your spiritual needs because this gives your life meaning and lets you know that you are doing right.

Keep your life in balance. Don't get complacent; continue to give yourself reality tests and attitude checks on a regular basis. It is easier than you think to let your awareness slip into old patterns. Of course, you must still avoid your addictive behavior. It is a rare addict who can sample his addictive behavior without getting hooked again. Why *ever* take that chance?

You are more likely to lapse when you are feeling tired, depressed, or sorry for yourself — or on the other hand, if you are feeling strong, self-satisfied, and overconfident. Try to stay flexible and tolerant of other people and their shortcomings; hold on to your humility. You have come a long way, but that doesn't make you Super Person. You are still a human being and likely to make mistakes as you continue through life. Be especially careful if you are taking prescription drugs; they may have extremely powerful and unexpected effects on you. And if you catch yourself being dishonest, **WATCH OUT!** If you can lie to other people, you can lie to yourself — and that is the road back to denial and addiction.

If you feel yourself slipping, go for a checkup session or make a group meeting. In other words, do all the things you have learned to help you take control. Even if you do relapse, **don't give up.** The greatest danger in slipping is that you may decide you've blown the whole thing and go right back into your addictive behavior. A slip is not uncommon. If you backslide, take charge! Just because you have slipped, you don't have to slide all the way to the bottom.

You can use your new skills and the help you have available to regain a rewarding, addiction-free life. If a slip happens, realize that it is a mistake, a normal human failing which you can correct. Use your lapse as a chance to learn and go on growing.

CHAPTER EIGHT

FOR THE FAMILY AND LOVED ONES

If you're like most families and friends, you have found yourself in a cycle right along with your addict. In some cases, you may have been through these problems before with some other addict in your life. Obviously you don't approve of the addictive behavior but you really don't know what can or should be done. You're hopeful when the addict stops using for a few days or gets a new job or promises that this is the last time. Then you're disappointed, disgusted, and/or angry when the latest hope doesn't pan out. The rollercoaster ride gets real old after awhile and you want OFF!

DEALING WITH THE FEAR

You have many fears which hold you back from taking positive action. Because you are not able to fix the situation or don't know the right thing to do, you usually do nothing. You may be afraid to risk losing your addict's love. Or maybe you're afraid that your actions could end the relationship and you might not be able to make it on your own. Once in awhile, the drunk stays home at night, the gambler sometimes wins and pays a bill, or the pot smoker makes a few repairs. You may see this as a sign of progress and be afraid that your actions will prevent the addict's recovery. Of course, the improvement doesn't last. An even deeper fear that we often don't recognize is that the addict *will* recover. That's scary because then you won't be so needed anymore.

Initially you try many things to get the addict to stop. You nag, you lay down guilt trips, you beg, you make threats that you don't carry out or at least don't carry out fully. None of these attempts has worked and you're deeply frustrated. Be aware that none of these efforts will **ever** work because *you can't change another person's behavior.* You can only change your own! Therefore, it is time to come out of the fog. It is time to take charge of **yourself.** The changes you make may or may not cause the addict to respond differently, but that can not be the reason for you to change. You need to change because you don't like the way **your** life is now.

BOUNDARIES AND LIMITS

Every human being must have *boundaries* between themselves and others. Inside these boundaries, you are responsible and you have the ability to influence what happens. Outside your boundaries, you cannot control what happens, and therefore you cannot take responsibility. Things outside your boundaries will have an effect on you. You can choose how you respond to them, but you can't control them. Living within your own boundaries makes you an individual. It defines your identity and frees you of the addict's behavior.

To maintain boundaries you must set limits. The proper way to set limits is to state where you draw the line and then show that you mean what you say. **You** decide what you will and will not do, what you will live with and what you choose not to live with. Obviously it is not "healthy" to act contrary to your best interest. Therefore, it is essential to set limits which offer the greatest potential for healthy, positive feelings and constructive actions.

When it comes to another person's behavior, there may seem to be little difference between saying, "If you don't stop, I will leave," and "I choose not to live with a person who is addicted." In the first case, what you do depends on what another person does. In the second, you are stating what you will do; you have already made your choice regardless of the other's choice. This is not a threat, just a statement of your own behavior. The addict then must make his or her choice about the addiction.

Setting Limits

The following illustration is an everyday example of setting limits. Sue is an alcoholic who does not recognize her addiction. Her husband Bill has done all the usual cover-ups of a co-dependent (see page 17). One Monday Bill tells Sue that friends have asked them over for a barbecue this Friday. She agrees to accept the invitation. On Friday morning Bill reminds Sue that they will have to leave by seven p.m. for the barbecue. Sue agrees and of course means to be home at seven. (It is necessary to remind Sue of the commitment: an addict needs information to make a good choice.) At seven that evening Sue has not come home. Bill goes to the barbecue. (He refuses to let Sue ruin his plans.) At 8:30, Sue arrives at the barbecue. It is obvious she has been drinking. She loudly announces that she had to work late and looks to Bill to back her up. He says nothing. (Bill refuses to support her cover-up.)

In this example, Bill refused to get himself involved in Sue's drinking behavior. He did not lecture, nag, or try to make her feel guilty. He just went ahead with his plans. Sue had to face the consequences of her own behavior. Bill may have had some bad moments worrying that Sue may have been in an accident due to her drinking, but staying home and worrying would not have caused nor prevented an accident. This action would be hard for Bill at first, but it gets easier each time.

Stand Your Ground

Having made your choice, you must present this information to the addict in a way that is direct and believable. When you state your limit, you are really saying, "I'm not going to support your addiction anymore." That does not mean you won't support recovery.

Supporting the *addiction* involves making excuses, covering up, and taking up the slack. Supporting the recovery means letting the addict bear the full consequences of his or her addiction, perhaps attending family meetings, not tempting the addict to try the addictive behavior again, showing interest in recovery, and learning more about addiction through groups such as Al-Anon or Ala-Teen. Other groups such as Narcotics Anonymous and Sex

Addicts Anonymous have similar family support groups.

The decision and follow-through required to stop supporting an addiction are almost as hard as the addict's struggle to give up his or her addiction. In many ways, the family of an addict must go through a change or recovery process very similar to that of the addict. Like the addict, the family member must change for him or herself. They must act to improve their own quality of life, rather than to change the addict's behavior. The addict still has the right and responsibility to make his or her own decision.

CHAPTER NINE

TAKING ACTION

All right, here we are, where the rubber meets the road! By now we've covered what addiction is, its effects and causes, barriers to change, the advantages of recovery, how to begin, and where to get help. Maybe this has caused you to do a lot of reflecting and, we hope, helped you decide to overcome addiction. Now it's time to take *action!* Here is where you have the chance to make this book useful in your life.

A NEW WINDOW INTO THE WORLD

"Every day I am addiction-free I can see myself and the world with greater clarity and depth. I'd forgotten how wonderful living can be."

Don't Die An Addict!

Understand: in most cases "addiction" is not a permanent condition we must live and die with. It is a mental frame of reference, a "window" through which we have learned to view the world. Perhaps we don't know any better because that's the way we were raised...or perhaps we've just grown into it because we lack other ways to handle reality. But now that we are awake to the truth, the question is not "why" or "if only," but "now what?"

Let Your Crutches Go!

An addictive crutch restricts your mental options just like a real crutch limits your physical range of movement. You can move with much more agility and speed when you quit relying on crutches. **All** crutches! It is slow going at first until you get your balance and confidence, but the advantages are well worth breaking through the pain and fear.

It's amazing to look at the wealth of benefits that result from breaking free from addiction! New doors to a better life begin to open. But simply knowing what can be gained from recovery is no **substitute** for ACTION! Good intentions mean nothing if you don't follow through. You have to *actually do it!*

All We Have is The NOW

After years of habitual behavior, when it comes time to really change, you may feel as though your feet are cast in concrete and unable to move. This is one of the ways an addiction keeps you under control. But much of that control is an illusion which fades a bit more with each small step a person takes into recovery.

There is NO benefit from waiting or delaying your recovery! Yesterday is "history" and there is no guarantee that tomorrow is on the calendar. All we have in this life is NOW. Right now is the only time we own, the only thing we can hope to control!

GET UP AND GET HELP

"If just 'thinking' about kicking would do the trick, I would have been clean years ago. The fact is you have to get off your dead ass and actually DO IT. There's no substitute for action."

You know by now there is no reward in being a slave to a habit. No matter what the addiction or how deeply you're caught up in it, it is not the end of the world! Even if your habit seems to be minor, do not discount it. Every form of addictive behavior does damage to your integrity and self-worth.

Again, keep in mind that you are not super human! You cannot simply fix yourself through will power! GO GET HELP! Find one or more caring, capable people who understand what you are going through and are willing to help you achieve your freedom. You **need** people who will tell you the truth, not just what you want to hear!

Come out of hiding! Confront yourself and your addiction with a strong heart. Make a decision, pick up the phone or go to a meeting, and REACH OUT. You will find that spark of understanding, love, and support you need. It won't be in the form of some magical overnight remedy. It took time to dig into the trap you're in and it will take time to build the ladder needed to climb out.

Also be aware that you will be called on to make many new and uncomfortable changes as you work to exercise control over your mind and life. The secrets are determination, self-discipline, and the willingness to keep on. NEVER DOUBT that it can be done. It is worth **whatever is necessary!**

Take That First Step

"After breaking my leg in seven places, it came time to take the first new step. I feared it would all come apart, but I had to try. It was short and quick but, by God, I did it!"

The first step is scary as hell — but the rush of knowing you can do it is one of the most rewarding personal achievements you will ever feel! Throwing away your crutches lets you know that you can solve problems in new and creative ways. That first effort and each one after it will free you just a bit more from your bondage. As former addicts, we may always be vulnerable to addictive behavior. But addiction does not have to be the focus of our lives forever. We can begin to fill in our days with new, fresh insight and experiences.

Therefore, you need not be a captive of the past or a victim of the future. Deal with TODAY by having the courage and honesty to face the facts of your dependencies. Commit yourself to walking the path of full recovery. You will come to terms with the truth as it IS and find the help to build a higher quality of life based on self-respect and achievement. No decision you ever make will be more important or rewarding!

Take that first step, then the second, and the third — and keep on walking!

THE BEGINNING

OPEN Information Series Materials

A Map Through the Maze

A psycho-social map of the criminal justice system from arrest to success. This tour of the "correctional experience" offers "insider" insight on how to obtain and maintain freedom through personal growth. Also includes compassionate advice for the families and loved ones of offenders.

99 Days & A Get Up

This survival guide for offenders and loved ones covers the months just before and after release from prison. Covers "short pains," false expectations, emotional adjustments to release, and family reunions. Can be used alone or with the following video.

Preparing for Success

A video introduction to the issues affecting success following release — an ideal attention-getter for pre-release and a prelude to *99 Days.* It looks at real people discussing their real feelings.

Life Without a Crutch

Gives down-to-earth reasons to overcome denial and seek recovery from addiction. Also offers practical advice on how and where to find help. Readers will identify with these scenarios and find encouragement on every page.

Man, I Need a Job!

Not the advice you would find in a post-college job search workbook. It's designed to help people with a record get a toehold in the community. Covers: disclosure of a criminal history; personal responsibility; locating job leads; applications, resumes, and interviews; finding community support; overcoming rejection; and keeping your new job.

Man, I Need a Job! — Spanish Edition

The same practical advice offered in the English edition, professionally translated into Spanish. This book will help Hispanic offenders find a job and develop a successful role in community life.

For ordering information, please contact:

OPEN, INC. • P.O. Box 566025 • Dallas, TX 75356-6025
(972) 271-1971 • 1-800-966-1966 • (972) 278-5884 Fax